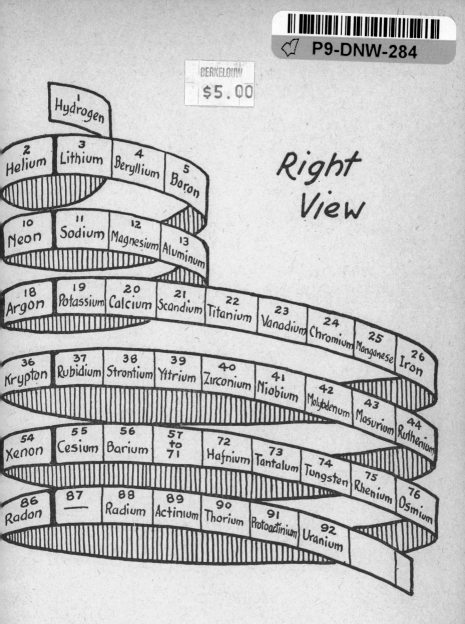

Right
View

OF THE ELEMENTS

EXPLAINING THE ATOM

EXPLAINING

THE ATOM

BY SELIG HECHT

PROFESSOR OF BIOPHYSICS
COLUMBIA UNIVERSITY

NEW YORK · THE VIKING PRESS · 1947

"There is no possibility of telling whether the issue of scientists' work will prove them to be fiends, or dreamers, or angels."

—LORD RAYLEIGH

For Celia

PREFACE

This is a book for the complete layman. It follows
the steps that were taken historically in going from the
earliest questions about the nature of common substances
to the large-scale liberation of atomic energy. The number of these steps is small, and the ideas involved are
simple. They can be described in all their essentials without assuming any knowledge of physics, chemistry, and
mathematics. I have done this before in five lectures at
the New School for Social Research in New York to an
audience most of whom had had no training in any science.
The steps are explicitly stated in the Table of Contents
and form a skeleton summary of the story.

The reader is urged to go through the book in a few
sessions. He is advised to read easily and steadily, and not
to struggle with any part that seems unclear; most likely it
will become clear later. The point is to read ahead and
to get the full sweep of the narrative. If after a first rapid
reading one has any impulse toward rereading, the tempta-
tion should not be resisted. The reward of a second reading
is disproportionately large in pleasure and profit.

I did not work on any project connected with the atomic bomb; my war work dealt with light and vision. My knowledge of atomic physics comes from public sources. All the scientific information secured before 1940 is available in books and professional articles. Between 1940 and 1945 papers on atomic physics were not published. Since then there has been the official Report on Atomic Energy by H. D. Smyth; and now there has begun again a slow trickle of professional papers. What I understand, thousands of professional people know. I hold no secrets.

This book could easily have been ten times its size with all the details, diagrams, and equations to make it scholarly and complete, and all without recourse to secret information. It is a thin book so that it will easily convey to the layman the intellectual drama of the developments in physics during the last fifty years. This needs no apparatus of scholarship.

My purpose is to supply a background against which people can think and act intelligently on the problems of atomic energy. So long as one supposes that this business is mysterious and secret, one cannot have a just evaluation of our possession and security. Only by understanding the basis and development of atomic energy can one judge the legislation and foreign policy that concern it. I hope that this book will help to make intelligent voters.

SELIG HECHT

Golden Farm, Bridgewater, Connecticut
September 10, 1946

CONTENTS

xi

LIST OF ILLUSTRATIONS

EXPLAINING THE ATOM

PROLOGUE

SCIENCE, SECRETS, AND THE ATOMIC BOMB

Before dawn on July 16, 1945, a group of scientists and military men met in a deserted region of New Mexico to make a scientific experiment. The men arranged themselves so that some were 25 miles from a central tower and some about 10 miles. The persons nearest the tower were in a timber and earth observation shelter 7 miles away.

At a given moment someone closed a switch that started a series of events controlled by machinery installed for this purpose. The end of this series was that at a prearranged moment there occurred a tremendous flash of light, followed immediately by a strong surge of heat, and some seconds later by a loud rumbling noise. One observer, who lay flat on the ground 10 miles from the explosion, with his head down and only his neck exposed, said that it felt as if a hot iron had been held next to his skin. The first atomic bomb had been exploded.

A few weeks later the next atomic bomb was exploded over Hiroshima, and a while later, a third over Nagasaki. Since then two more have been exploded, at Bikini. We have all become familiar with the appearance of the events: the mushroom-shaped cloud rising 40,000 feet, the shattered houses, and the distorted factories.

In Hiroshima 50,000 people were killed immediately, and of those who survived a like number died soon after. Months later, some were still dying. There is no way of knowing how long the effects of this bomb will last. We do not know how many people have been made sterile by the intense x-rays, nor what will appear in future Japanese who will be the children of those exposed to x-rays but not visibly injured.

Since those fateful weeks the world has had no rest from the atomic bomb, as its international and domestic implications have become clearer to an astonished but unprepared public. The multitude of articles, pamphlets, and discussions has dissipated the more absurd ideas about atomic energy, and has exposed the real problems and some of their possible solutions. But many ridiculous ideas remain, particularly those concerning the origin, the nature, and the secrets of atomic energy.

In some experience with atomic energy legislation, I have talked with enough public men to know that almost none of them understand even the elementary principles underlying the release of atomic energy. The same is true for most well-educated laymen. And yet all of us must make decisions about this weapon, which "is potentially destructive beyond the wildest nightmare of the imagination." These decisions cannot be made in ignorance; the public must be informed.

Consider the matter of secrets, of which there is still too much talk. As will become apparent there is no unique or single secret about atomic energy or even about the bomb. However, among the many bills introduced into Congress, one even provided the death penalty for giving away *the* secret of the atomic bomb. Such behavior assumes that the release of atomic energy happened suddenly without any previous history. Indeed, many people still believe this, and the newspaper stories have helped to encourage such belief. There lingers among us the idea that an inventor, a scientist, a professor, is a long-haired gentleman, a little wild in the head, who has crazy ideas which occasionally work out. The atomic bomb presumably was one of those that worked.

As a matter of fact the scientists on the Manhattan Project were generally known as the longhairs. One of my friends who was a consultant for the atomic bomb project began to make regular visits to the barber and to take them very seriously. He explained that as a professor his hair made little difference to him or to his colleagues as long as it looked decent; but when he had to deal with the Army men, he insisted that at least the physical excuse for being called a longhair should be absent.

The popular story has it that one of these longhairs, seconded by no less a longhair than Albert Einstein, managed to tell President Roosevelt about his idea for an atomic bomb. He estimated the cost at about two billion dollars, and the President, being a sporting man with excellent judgment, took this gigantic gamble, and appointed a general to direct the production of the bomb. The general then hired scientists and engineers, and built laboratories and factories; and sure enough, he constructed a bomb, to the discomfiture of the Japanese and the greater glory of American industry.

This whole conception—the secret of the longhair, the President's gamble, and the position of the general—is wrong. It is wrong for several reasons. The notion of atomic energy is nothing new; it has been investigated and discussed by thousands of people for years. Even the actual words have long been in use. For about 50 years scientists have been working in this area, and innumerable papers have been published about it. As we shall see, the subject has had an orderly history and development, which a host of people all over the world knew and understood. The particular longhair who proposed the idea to the President will not be disturbed by the statement that physicists in Denmark, England, France, and Germany had similar ideas at the same time and actually began to work on them.

The newspaper conception is dangerous, as well as wrong, because it gives the impression that two billion dollars can buy us anything we wish. If for two billion dollars we can buy the utilization of atomic energy and the construction of atomic bombs when none existed before, then surely for two billion dollars we can cure cancer and eradicate heart disease and other scourges. Let's go! Let's raise the money, get a director, hire the scientists, and all will be well.

We should know that all the money in the world could not have built an atomic bomb in 1936. Atomic energy was known, and many of its properties were understood. It had been released in small quantities in laboratories, and its release in large quantities in the sun and the stars had been studied. But the critical information and the critical direction to follow for releasing it in large amounts on earth were lacking in 1936, and no one could have used two billion dollars for making an atomic bomb at that time. It is this that is important in understanding the relation of science to industry, to medicine, and to the public. There has to be knowledge before it can be applied. At a certain stage of scientific development, theoretically critical knowledge becomes available. Before that moment—which no one can guarantee in advance—the knowledge cannot be applied. After that moment application is reasonably certain and only the special technics for its utilization need be worked out.

What is it that we learned in 1939 that we did not know in 1936? What rendered it feasible to try making an atomic bomb in 1939, the lack of which would have prevented making an atomic bomb in 1935? It was uranium fission and the associated release of neutrons. But these words are meaningless by themselves. And so too are all the other words like isotopes, Einstein's equation, protons, and plutonium that are currently found in newspaper reports.

The things and ideas for which these words stand were not discovered by the Manhattan District; they did not suddenly arrive on the scene. They arose during the continuous growth and development of a segment of science that forms one of the most fascinating chapters in the history of the human race. To extend Isaac Newton's metaphor, the development of a bomb by the release of atomic energy is merely the latest impact of the wave of physical science that began about fifty years ago on the ocean of knowledge. To understand atomic energy one must know the origin, the course, and the properties of that wave. And that means understanding the structure of the atom.

I

THE ATOM AS A HOMOGENEOUS BALL

1. WHY ATOMS?

When we speak of *atomic* energy and the *atomic* bomb, most of us know vaguely that these new and violent forces come from the internal structure of the atom. There we stop, because as laymen we do not even know why we assume the existence of atoms, let alone what their complicated internal workings are.

Why do we speak of atoms? Why do we say that matter is made up of a host of atoms? Objects like the table and the chair, and substances like iron and sugar, appear to be continuous. Water looks as if it were continuous, and so does the glass that contains it; otherwise the water would come through the glass.

Nevertheless, even Democritus in 400 B.C. suspected that the continuous appearance of objects and substances is not a revelation of their true structure, and he suggested that matter is basically discontinuous. He supposed it to be made up of exceedingly small parts, so small that they cannot be made any smaller. These he called atoms. Why did Democritus conceive such a curious idea?

Simple and common experience can give the answer. Ordinary table salt dissolves and disappears when put into water. So does sugar in coffee, and so do hundreds of common substances when placed in water or other liquids. If water were as continuous as it appears to be, there would be no room for the salt and sugar to disappear into. There must be holes in water; many, many holes. Moreover, salt and sugar must be made up of very tiny particles that can get into these holes and disappear.

Another experience shows this even more strikingly. Take a glass of water and put a crystal of any colored dye on the bottom. Very slowly, even without stirring, the dye dissolves and gradually spreads throughout the water. To hasten the process we stir the water and the dye, and end with an evenly colored solution in the glass. Surely both the water and the dye must be made up of microscopic particles that can mingle and occupy the spaces between them.

Take another common observation. A quart of water when mixed with a quart of alcohol produces less than two quarts of mixture. Part of the alcohol works its way into the spaces between the water particles, and part of the water works its way between the alcohol particles.

These things happen not only in water and other liquids. They occur in air and even in solids. Our neighbor's bacon frying in the morning liberates something that can diffuse into the air and finally reach our nostrils. Clearly there must be holes in the air, spaces where there are no air particles, so that the odoriferous fragments from the bacon can push through and reach us yards away.

If a bar of gold with a sharp clean edge is put in close contact with the similarly clean edge of a bar of silver, and the two bars are pressed together for several months, and then separated, some gold can be found inside the silver bar and some silver inside the gold bar. Particles of gold and silver have migrated across the boundary. Solids can diffuse into other solids, just as gases diffuse into other gases, and solids dissolve in liquids.

All this tells us that appearance is not reality; that what we can see is only a superficial continuity of matter; that fundamentally there are innumerable holes in all sub-stances, even the most solid. We explain these holes by supposing them to be the spaces between the ultimate small particles, the atoms, that compose matter.

2. ATOMS AND MOLECULES

The phenomena of diffusion and interpenetration are excellent reasons for assuming the existence of atoms. However, there are even better ones, and these better ones give further insight into the nature of atoms. To understand these reasons we must learn something more about the properties of matter.

It is well to start with common things like wood, bread, beans, cheese, sugar, and hair. When these materi-als are burned or charred they yield charcoal or carbon. Examination shows that this carbon when cleaned and purified is the same regardless of its origin. The question as to whether the carbon was in the wood and sugar all the time, or whether it was produced by the process of burning was settled long ago. We know that the carbon was there originally. Later it will be clear why.

If we now try to change the carbon by boiling it with acids, or with ammonia and other alkalis, with benzine, or with dozens of other agents, nothing happens to the carbon. It always comes back as carbon. There is almost nothing that can be done with carbon to change its appearance and properties; it remains carbon. Even if it is heated in air, and slowly disappears as a gas, the gas can be caught, and carbon can be got back from it.

Carbon is thus a substance that enters into the composition of a variety of more complex materials ranging from butter to marble; it can always be pulled out of these materials to assume its typical carbon appearance and properties; and it cannot be transformed into any simpler material. Carbon, therefore, is an irreducible, an elementary substance.

In the same way that carbon emerges from a variety of complex materials, other elementary substances such as zinc, copper, gold, sulfur, hydrogen, helium, iron, and mercury can be derived from the innumerable materials in the world. Each possesses unique properties; each differs from the other elementary substances; and each retains its individuality. No chemical procedures can transform one of these elementary substances into another. The most violent chemical actions cannot change carbon into gold, or sulfur into mercury, or lead into silver. They are irreducible elementary substances. By 1940 there were 92 of these substances known. They are called the chemical elements, or more briefly, elements.

All the infinite variety of materials in the world is made up of combinations of these elements, by twos, threes, fours, and even fives. Thus sugar is made of carbon, hydrogen, and oxygen; marble of calcium, carbon, and oxygen; sand of silicon and oxygen; and so on forever with the rest of the 92 elements.

Since each of these elementary substances is irreducible and unique, and we have already assumed that all matter is made up of atoms, it seems sensible to suppose that the atoms that compose each element are themselves unique. In this way we can think of atoms of copper, carbon, gold, silver, hydrogen, and aluminum as special, each to its own kind. Indeed, we must assume 92 different species of atoms corresponding to the 92 chemical elements. The justification and the consequences of this assumption form the burden of our story, and will emerge as we develop it.

All the things in the world are made up of combinations of the chemical elements. Objects such as rocks, chairs, lampshades, and rugs are built of materials like marble, wood, iron, parchment, cotton, and wool. Some of these materials have a complicated structure of their own. Wood, for example, is not the same all through. It has grain, formed by the alternation of hard and soft fibers, and the varieties of wood depend on this visible organization. Wood is therefore an inhomogeneous substance; it cannot be purified and rendered completely homogeneous. However, the essential ingredient of wood is cellulose, which can be purified and prepared so as to be uniform throughout. Such purified, reproducible, and homogeneous materials are called pure substances, and there are hundreds of thousands of them. Sugar is one; table salt another. Aluminum, iron, calomel, bicarbonate of soda, lime, penicillin, diamond, alcohol, and DDT are examples of substances that can be prepared in pure form, so that any small fragment is like any other fragment.

When this vast array of pure substances is examined chemically, it can be divided into two kinds. First there is the small group of 92 elementary substances like iron, aluminum, and carbon, which we already know about. They cannot be decomposed by any chemical treatment. And second, there is the remaining, enormous group, containing substances that can be decomposed chemically to yield some of the 92 elements. These pure but decomposable substances are compounded from the elements, and are known as chemical compounds.

The nature of these compounds and their formation may be illustrated by the behavior of iron and sulfur. Both iron and sulfur are elements, and both are solids. If we grind them into fine powders and mix them thoroughly, they are still iron and sulfur. With a microscope the particles of sulfur and the particles of iron can be seen as separate and differently colored. If now the mixture is heated, the recurring miracle of chemistry takes place. The heated mass becomes transformed. The two separate substances disappear, and a new substance appears, made up of both iron and sulfur. This is iron sulfide, which looks, behaves, and dissolves differently from either iron or sulfur. It can be cleaned and purified, and is a compound substance uniform throughout. Iron sulfide occurs in nature as crystals, and is known as fool's gold because of its superficial resemblance to gold.

What is the ultimate structure of such compounds? They too must be built up of extremely small particles, because they too can dissolve and diffuse in liquids. In fact, our first examples of this behavior were compounds like sugar and salt. The supposition is that in compounds the ultimate particles are built up of atoms of the elements that form the compounds. In this way an atom of sulfur and an atom of iron unite to form a new unit, a molecule of iron sulfide. The smallest unit of a compound is a molecule.

Molecules are made up of atoms of one or more of the 92 elements. Because it is easy to break up compounds into their constituent elements, it must be that the atoms in the molecule maintain most of their individuality. No matter how complex the compound, no matter how large its molecule, one can always get back the constituent elements. In other words, molecules can be separated into their component atoms.

At this point, it is well to remember that this talk about atoms and molecules is theory. No one has ever seen an atom or a molecule, even with the highest power of the microscope. They are much too small. Atoms and molecules are concepts of the human mind, and are used to explain the behavior of ordinary substances in bulk. The idea is that if we assume matter to be composed of invisible atoms and molecules, then a lot of events that are visible become understandable. The more we learn about the properties of matter and the behavior of different substances, the more illuminating and the more reasonable is this relatively simple notion that substances are made up of atoms and molecules.

The procedure is something like this. We observe phenomena like diffusion, like the nontransformation of elementary substances, like the homogeneity of compounds and the ease of their decomposition into elementary substances. In order to explain these observations we assume the existence of atoms and molecules. Then we say that if atoms and molecules are what we think they are, ordinary substances should have certain definite properties that we can predict. If the predicted properties turn out to be correct, we have strengthened the reasons for believing in the reality of atoms and molecules. This reciprocal development of information and explanation is the essence of science; and in the particular field with which we are concerned, namely atomic structure, the development has been simple, logical, and frequently dramatic.

3. THE WEIGHTS OF ATOMS

The differences between elements and compounds became clear toward the end of the eighteenth century; and in 1780 Antoine Lavoisier, the great chemist who died in the French Revolution, was able to list nearly 50 known elements. In working with elements and compounds, Lavoisier established the fundamental fact that during all the transformations of one substance into another, and of compounds into elements and the reverse, there is no loss in total weight of material involved. This is the principle of the conservation of matter. Regardless of what you do to substances, no matter how their properties change as they react with each other, no matter how different they look afterward, you end with the same total weight of matter with which you started.

As an example actually studied by Lavoisier, we can consider a burning candle. When a candle burns, it disappears and in its place gases are formed. In addition, the air surrounding the candle becomes changed so that it is no longer fit to breathe. Lavoisier knew that the hot wax of the candle combined with the oxygen of the surrounding air (which he called free air) to form water vapor and carbon dioxide (which he called fixed air). We can write this in the form of an equation as

Candle + free air = fixed air + water vapor.

Lavoisier measured the weight of the candle that disappeared and the weight of the oxygen that combined with it, and found their sum to equal the weight of the carbon dioxide and the water vapor or moisture that were formed.

In the conservation of matter during chemical reactions it makes no difference whether the beginning substances are gas or solid or liquid, and it makes no difference whether the end products are gas or solid or liquid. The important thing is to measure everything that enters into the reaction and to catch everything that forms during the reaction. If you do that, you find that there is no loss of matter. The equation balances.

The observed conservation of matter is easily translated in terms of the theoretical atoms and molecules. It says that atoms contain all the mass of any substance, and that regardless of the ways in which the atoms join to form molecules, they carry their individual masses with them. This is a revealing generalization; but the experiments that followed its formulation were even more revealing of the nature of matter. It turned out that when elements combine to form compounds they always do so in definite proportions.

For example, when you burn coal or carbon you find that by weight 3 parts of carbon always combine with 8 parts of oxygen. Thus 3 ounces of carbon as it burns takes out 8 ounces of oxygen from the surrounding air. Similarly, when hydrogen in air is transformed into water vapor, the weight of oxygen consumed in the process is always 8 times the weight of the hydrogen. By the same token, if you examine any pure chemical compound like sugar, water, carbon dioxide, marble, or sulfadiazine, you always find that the elements in them exist in definite proportions by weight. From 11 pounds of carbon dioxide you can always get 3 pounds of carbon and 8 pounds of oxygen; and from 9 pounds of water you can always collect 1 pound of hydrogen and 8 pounds of oxygen.

The idea of definite proportions in the combination of elements or in the composition of compounds seems natural to us now. But it is important to put ourselves back 150 years. At that time all that Lavoisier and the other chemists knew was that air in which a candle could burn and which was fit for breathing was rendered unfit for either job after several candles had been burned in it. The "free" air had become "fixed" air; and the chemist's problem was to find out how "fixing" air rendered it useless for burning candles and for animal breathing. It was a revelation to find that the burning candle abstracted a definite amount of material—oxygen —from the air and produced in the process a given quantity of a new substance—carbon dioxide.

The recognition of the fact that when substances combine with each other they do so in definite proportions by weight marked the emergence of chemistry as a science. It made possible the next giant step forward in understanding the nature of matter. This step was taken in 1808 by John Dalton, who formulated the modern atomic theory. The original atomic idea of Democritus was philosophically basic, but practically vague. He had suggested that matter is discontinuous and composed of indivisible atoms. Dalton started from here and built a clearly formulated, scientific, working hypothesis.

Dalton proposed the idea that an element, since it is made of atoms, has all its atoms alike. All atoms of carbon are identical; all atoms of hydrogen are identical; all atoms of iron are identical. He further suggested that the atoms of different elements differ in weight. The atom of oxygen is heavier than that of hydrogen, and the atom of iron is heavier than that of oxygen. When atoms combine with other atoms by twos or threes, they remain unchanged in the molecule, and each molecule of a compound contains a definite number of atoms. The weight of a molecule therefore is the sum of the weights of its constituent atoms. At once it becomes clear why when elements combine they must do so in definite proportions.

Since this is a practical scientific theory, let us see where it leads. Consider carbon dioxide. We know that when carbon and oxygen combine to form carbon dioxide, 3 parts by weight of carbon combine with 8 parts of oxygen. This is shown in Figure 1. Suppose now, that during the formation of the carbon dioxide molecule, 1 atom of carbon combines with 2 atoms of oxygen. Then together the 2 oxygen atoms weigh 8 units of mass compared with the carbon atom, which weighs 3 units. If 2 oxygen atoms weigh 8 units, then each oxygen atom must weigh 4 units compared with the carbon atom of 3 units. This ratio of 3:4 in the relative weights of carbon and

	Reaction	Carbon	+ Oxygen	= Carbon Dioxide
Fact	*In Bulk* (pounds)	3	+ 8	= 11
	Combining weights	3	+ 8	= 11
Theory	Atoms	●	◯◯	= ◯◯◯
	Equation	C	+ 2 O	= CO₂
	Relative weights	3	+ 2×4	= 11
	Atomic and molecular Weights	12	+ 2×16	= 44

FIGURE 1. THE BURNING OF COAL OR CARBON

When carbon and oxygen combine during the burning of coal they do so in definite proportions, weight for weight. These proportions are accounted for by the atomic theory in terms of the constituent atoms and their weights. From the behavior of matter in bulk we deduce the properties of its atoms.

oxygen can be written as 6:8 or 12:16. The reason for writing it as 12:16 will be apparent in a moment when we consider water.

Water contains by weight 1 part of hydrogen to 8 parts of oxygen. Now suppose there are 2 atoms of hydrogen combined with each atom of oxygen in a molecule of water. The 2 hydrogen atoms together therefore weigh

1 unit, and each weighs ½ a unit. The relative weights of hydrogen and oxygen atoms must be as ½:8; and this ratio obviously can be written as 1:16.

Now let us set an arbitrary value of 16 units of mass as the weight of 1 oxygen atom. Then from these ratios it follows that the weight of a hydrogen atom is 1, and the weight of a carbon atom is 12. Notice that these relative weights of the atoms of hydrogen, carbon, and oxygen have been derived from the definite proportions by weight in which these elements in bulk combine to form carbon dioxide and water. This was part of Dalton's hypothesis. He suggested that the atoms of different elements differ in weight in the same relative way as do the combining weights of the elements when they form compounds. We have a fact and a theory. The fact is that when elements combine to form compounds they do so in definite proportions, known as their combining weights. The theory is that these relative weights are dependent on the relative weights of the atoms out of which the elements are composed.

In presenting these ideas here I have used whole numbers for the combining weights. This is not merely because it is convenient but also because it is correct as a first approximation. But only as a first approximation; and this too is of interest.

In Dalton's day the combining weights of a number of elements had been worked out with fair accuracy; and by assigning oxygen the arbitrary atomic weight of 16, the atomic weights of the known elements had been established. It is instructive to arrange the elements in the order of their atomic weights. The first 12 that were then known are as follows:

Hydrogen	H	1.01
Lithium	Li	6.94
Beryllium	Be	9.02
Boron	B	10.82
Carbon	C	12.01
Nitrogen	N	14.01
Oxygen	O	16.00
Fluorine	F	19.00
Sodium	Na	23.00
Magnesium	Mg	24.32
Aluminum	Al	26.97
Silicon	Si	28.06

Notice in this series that with the exception of magnesium the atomic weights are nearly but not quite whole numbers. It is almost as if they were regular multiples of hydrogen, which has an atomic weight of practically 1. This fascination of integral multiples and whole numbers has never left the problem of atomic weights. In fact, it dominated the scene for a while when William Prout, a contemporary of Dalton, actually did suppose that all elements were made up of hydrogen. Prout's hypothesis had to be discarded because the facts persisted in showing that the atomic weights were rarely whole numbers and always contained some values beyond the decimal point. We shall find as we go on with this story that the interest in whole numbers appears again and again as each new generalization and each new series of facts become available. Then, careful measurements show that the expected whole numbers do not materialize, and the differences between reality and expectation force us to look for new phenomena in the behavior and structure of atoms and molecules.

4. ATOMS IN SERIAL ORDER

Dalton's atomic theory was formulated at the beginning of the nineteenth century, and served as a powerful stimulus to hunt for as many elements as possible. By the middle of the century about 75 had been isolated and studied, and their properties had become common chemical knowledge. The first thing that became apparent was that the elements differed in atomic weight, and could be placed in serial order, much as we arranged the first 12 in the preceding section.

Another observation was that some elements were similar to others, and the similar elements seemed to occur in groups of three. The oldest and most familiar of these triads is copper, silver, and gold, whose similarities have been known for centuries. A less familiar group of three is lithium, sodium, and potassium. These are metals that are soft and shiny when freshly purified, but tarnish rapidly on exposure. In pure form all three react violently with water and therefore have to be kept immersed in kerosene. Moreover, they can be substituted for one another in compounds, and the resulting compounds are similar. Thus sodium chloride, or ordinary table salt, is white, crystalline, salty, and is easily dissolved in water. So is lithium chloride; and so is potassium chloride.

Early in the nineteenth century groups of similar elements had been found only in threes. They were called triads, and some remnant of the medieval mystery of the number 3 hung over them. However, some of the triads were purely accidental, because all the elements were not known. As more elements were discovered and isolated, groups began to include not only 3 but 4, 5, and sometimes 6 elements that behaved alike.

Such groups of similar elements were indeed tantalizing. Why should elements of such diverse atomic weights as 63.6, 107.9, and 197.2 be as similar as copper, silver, and gold? And why should two elements as similar in atomic weight as 32.1 and 35.5 be as different as sulfur and chlorine—a yellow solid and a green gas? Many were the speculations and guesses; many were the arrangements to which the elements were subjected—all to little avail until the year 1869. It was then that Dmitri I. Mendeléev, the Russian chemist, arranged the elements in a pattern known as the Periodic Table, which not only unified all the chemical information about them, but served as well to predict the properties of undiscov-

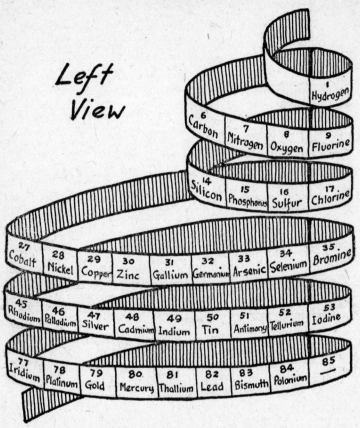

Left View

FIGURE 2. THE PERIODIC TABLE

The 92 elements have been arranged in size places on a ribbon, and coiled in a helix. As a result, elements with similar properties fall one under the other vertically. The figure shows two views of the coiled ribbon so that one can see it from both sides at the same time.

ered elements. Since then the Periodic Table has been the central core around which all chemical and physical knowledge of the elements have grown. It has served as

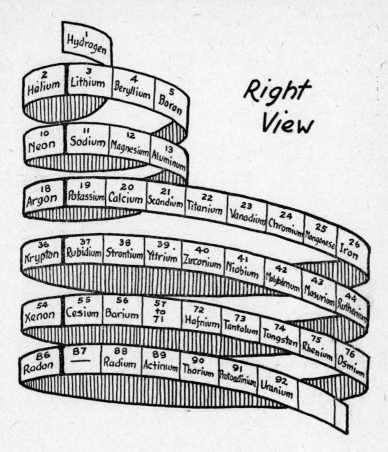

Right View

explanation and as inspiration, and in terms of it there has developed the beautiful edifice that is modern atomic physics and chemistry.

The first procedure in constructing the Periodic Table is to write down on a continuous ribbon according to their atomic weights the 92 elements from hydrogen to uranium, and to number them from 1 to 92. Next mark off with a heavy line successive segments of the ribbon so that the first segment contains 2 elements; the second and third segments contain 8 elements each; the fourth and fifth segments contain 18 elements each; the sixth segment contains 32 elements; and the seventh segment contains the remaining 6 through uranium.

Now take the ribbon of elements and coil it in a descending helix so that each segment begins and ends in the same vertical line. Thus the first elements of the segments are one under the other, and the last elements of the segments are also one under the other. The result is the Periodic Table shown in Figure 2 and in the end papers. The ribbon is drawn as viewed from the left and also from the right, so that it may be read continuously. The first segment, because it holds only 2 elements, has to be coiled tightly. Even so, hydrogen and helium need to be separated somewhat; hydrogen is put in twice for reasons that will become clear later. Note also that elements 57 to 71 have been jammed into one place; actually they jut out in a secondary small coil of their own, which is of no interest to us in this story.

The segments of the Periodic Table contain 2, 8, 18, or 32 elements. These numbers are not arbitrary; they are 2 times the squares of 1, 2, 3, and 4, respectively. The square of 1 is 1, which multiplied by 2 equals 2. The square of 2 is 4, which multiplied by 2 equals 8. The square of 3 is 9, which multiplied by 2 equals 18. The square of 4 is 16, which multiplied by 2 gives 32. This simple numerical series was not known to Mendeléev; we shall learn more about it later.

A host of interesting relations becomes evident in the Periodic Table. The first segment-coil begins with hydrogen and ends with helium, which is an inert gas. The next segment-coil begins with lithium, the soft metal we have already discussed, and ends with neon, another inert gas, used in illuminated signs. The third coil begins with sodium, a metal like lithium, and ends with argon, another inert gas, also used in signs. The fourth coil begins with potassium, another of the soft metals, takes in more elements than the preceding coil, and ends with krypton, which is still another inert gas, much like helium, neon, and argon. The fifth segment begins with rubidium, which like sodium and potassium is a soft metal, and ends with xenon, a gas like neon and helium. In short, all the elements in the first vertical column are similar, and all the elements in the terminal column are similar.

Precisely the same is true of the other vertical columns, even the short ones. Note our old friends the triad of copper, silver, and gold under element 29. Or take the elements next to these: zinc, cadmium, and mercury, which form a triad of similar metals known from the days of the alchemists. Now skip to the column formed by the penultimate elements of each coil: fluorine, chlorine, bromine, and iodine. Even the most uninitiated knows that the first three are noxious gases and that iodine easily becomes a smelly gas at ordinary temperature.

Perhaps the most curious series of elements is in the vertical column under helium. All are gases, and all were unknown and even unsuspected at the time of Mendeléev. They were discovered after 1890 by Lord Rayleigh and William Ramsay. With the exception of radon they occur normally in the air in very minute amounts. They are called noble gases because they do not combine with any other elements; they act as if they are completely satisfied with themselves. Most other elements combine relatively easily with others. The noble gases stand alone. There they are at the end of each coil one under the other.

When Mendeléev first arranged the Periodic Table only about 75 elements were known. Therefore, it was not so easy to see the regularities as it is now. Many empty spaces had to be put in, and it required an original feat of creative imagination to arrange the available elements in this regular and intelligible series. Mendeléev, however, did more than this. He had the intellectual courage to predict not merely the existence of these missing elements but also their quantitative properties. In every instance his predictions were verified, with remarkable accuracy.

As an example of this prediction, consider spot 32 in the fourth horizontal coil of the Periodic Table. This element lies in the vertical column between silicon and tin, and is now called germanium. Mendeléev in 1871 predicted its existence and called it eka-silicon. He said it would be grayish-white in color, would give a white oxide when burned in air, and would not be affected by acids or by alkalis. Moreover, he gave definite values for its atomic weight, its density, its atomic volume, and even its boiling point. Fifteen years later, when Clemens Winkler discovered and isolated it, he found Mendeléev's predictions almost perfectly fulfilled. Winkler called the element germanium for obvious national reasons, as is commonly done.

Prediction always appears mysterious. But quantitative prediction of the properties of unknown elements appears doubly mysterious. Sometimes the process is relatively easy and obvious; sometimes it involves a kind of inspired guessing that only a person of considerable scientific experience can do. In the present case it depends on the fact that the properties of the elements are periodic; similar properties occur at regular intervals when the elements are arranged in the order of atomic weights.

A simple example would be if one of the elements in the vertical column under lithium were not known. One could say in advance that it must be a soft metal since all the others in that column are like that. One could also say that it must be an alkali metal, which does not exist free in the natural state, because it is easily changed in the air and reacts violently with water. These are the properties of lithium, sodium, potassium, rubidium, and cesium. Therefore, if one of these were missing, its obvious properties could be predicted.

The more detailed and quantitative predictions require

closer study. The drawing in Figure 3 shows the relation that various elements have to a property known as the atomic volume, which is the volume or space occupied by an element as a solid in an amount of grams (1/28 ounce) equal to its atomic weight. Thus the atomic volume is the volume taken up by 6.94 grams of lithium, 9.02 grams of beryllium, 12.01 grams of carbon, and so on. In the drawing it is apparent that this property goes through cycles as the elements increase in atomic weight. The maximal atomic volume in each cycle is attained by the metals of the column in the Periodic Table under lithium, and includes sodium, potassium, rubidium, and cesium. The values for the other elements lie on the slopes and valleys between these peaks. Obviously, after the atomic weight of an unknown element has been estimated, it is easy to calculate its probable atomic volume merely by picking its position on the periodic graph in Figure 3.

When Mendeléev made the Periodic Table there were many empty spaces in it. He was able to construct the table only by putting similar elements into the same vertical columns. Nearly all the empty spaces have now been filled, and the elements can be arranged in succession from 1 to 92 as we have done. This numbering of the elements in sequence has turned out to be a property even more useful than the atomic weight. Each element thus has an atomic number recording its location in the sequence from hydrogen to uranium. The Periodic Table then shows that elements with similar characteristics occur at regular intervals of 2, 8, 18, or 32 elements apart.

It is tempting to ask what these numbers mean and

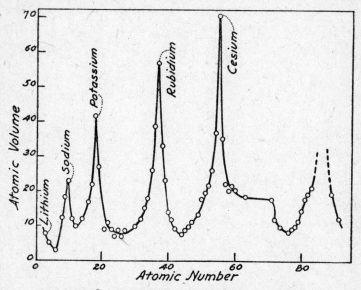

FIGURE 3. ATOMIC VOLUME AND ATOMIC NUMBER

Notice the regular way in which the atomic volume rises and falls as the elements grow heavier; notice also how the soft alkali metals all lie on the peaks while the other elements fall in between.

what this periodicity tells us. They must surely be an expression of the internal structure of the atom. However, even at the end of the nineteenth century no one knew anything about the inside of atoms. When a chemist or a physicist thought of an atom he considered it a solid sphere like a billiard ball, relatively hard and uniform throughout.

Even now this concept of an atom is useful for most

work in chemistry. The organic chemist who builds complicated molecules like those of DDT or penicillin or rubber rarely thinks of the atom in any other way. The mineralogist still uses this concept whenever he wishes

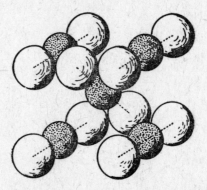

FIGURE 4. A CRYSTAL OF SOLID CARBON DIOXIDE OR DRY ICE

Notice how each carbon atom (stippled) always has two oxygen atoms attached to it. A large crystal contains millions of such units arranged in this orderly geometrical way.

to describe the crystal structure of a compound. Figure 4 is a picture of the kind repeatedly employed for making visual the make-up of chemical compounds. It is a diagram of solid carbon dioxide. The arrangement of the atoms in the molecule accounts for the properties of the compounds.

II

THE ATOM BECOMES COMPLEX

1. THE SURFACE OF ATOMS

Even before the end of the nineteenth century many chemists knew that the concept of the atom as a homogeneous elastic ball was merely a useful fiction. It explained a tremendous amount about the structure of matter, but it could not be true. There were several reasons for this, and the investigation of the reasons furnished new information that helped clarify and expand our ideas about atoms.

The most potent doubt about the complete homogeneity of atoms comes from the fact that atoms join with each other to form molecules. Billiard balls do not stick to each other, or enter into stable combinations by twos and threes. But atoms do; and because they combine, their surfaces must have special arrangements for holding on tightly to one another. Chemists called these holding devices, bonds; and they soon found consistent regularities in the number and strength of the bonds that different elements possess.

An atomic bond can be defined as the capacity of an

atom to hold a hydrogen atom or its equivalent. For example, an oxygen atom can hold 2 hydrogen atoms as in H_2O, water; therefore it has 2 bonds. A carbon atom can hold 4 hydrogen atoms as in methane, CH_4, and therefore it has 4 bonds. Moreover, since each oxygen atom has 2 bonds, carbon can hold 2 oxygen atoms, as in carbon dioxide, which is CO_2. A nitrogen atom can hold 3 hydrogen atoms as in ammonia, NH_3, and therefore has 3 bonds.

Elements in the same vertical column of the Periodic Table have the same number of atomic bonds. Often these bonds are spoken of as valences, especially when the elements rather than their atoms are referred to. In this way, hydrogen is single valent, or monovalent; oxygen is divalent; nitrogen, trivalent; and carbon, tetravalent.

All chemical reactions consist of the transformation of molecular species into one another. For example, when wood burns, the complex molecule of cellulose, which contains atoms of carbon, hydrogen, and oxygen, is transformed by combination with more oxygen atoms from the air into molecules of water and carbon dioxide. By means of their bonds the atoms in molecules can be rearranged into new combinations of atoms to produce different molecules.

Some bonds are tighter than others. The tighter they are, the more stable are the compounds. The looser the bonds, the less stable are the compounds and the more likely are they to break apart with the release of energy. Thus when atoms change their affiliations with other atoms the process may require energy or it may give off energy, depending on the stability of the initial and final products. Therefore some chemical reactions will take place only with the addition of energy in the form of heat or electricity from the outside, while other reactions give off heat or electricity.

Ultimately all the energy we use comes from the light of the sun. Green plants absorb this light and use it as energy with which to build up compounds of carbon, hydrogen, and oxygen. The carbon-hydrogen combination involves bonds that are loose, and it is therefore particularly high in energy. It is present in gasoline, sugar, starch, wood, and the like, and when these are used as fuels the carbon-hydrogen combination is replaced by a carbon-oxygen combination that is tighter, and therefore much lower in energy. The difference in energy between the two combinations is given off and furnishes us with motor power and heat.

Even explosives like TNT act only by the energy released by their bonds in the rearrangement of its component elements. When TNT explodes, its large molecule is first broken into small molecules like carbon dioxide, water vapor, and nitrogen gas, which contain much less energy in their bond combinations than the original molecule. The difference in energy is released as heat, which acts on these gases to expand them suddenly. It is this sudden expansion that is the explosion.

What are these surface structures, these bonds? Obviously a bond is not a hook that one atom sticks into another. If this were so, there would be aggressive atoms and passive atoms, and there is no evidence for this. The behavior of the elements is such that, in water for example, it is just as correct to say that 1 oxygen atom holds 2 hydrogen atoms as that 2 hydrogen atoms hold 1 oxygen atom between them. Bonds represent reciprocal arrangements between atoms. When 2 atoms are joined, each atom undoubtedly contributes something to the bond holding them together.

But what is this that each atom contributes to make the bond that ties it to another atom? For years no one knew. Chemists generally were satisfied with the idea, of bonds without caring much about its ultimate meaning. In fact, the answer to the question did not come from chemistry, but from electricity. And when the answer came it far transcended the original question, because it helped our understanding of many other phenomena beside atomic structure.

2. ELECTRONS FROM THE SURFACE OF ATOMS

The ancient Greeks knew that when an amber rod is rubbed with cloth or fur, the amber becomes electrically charged, and is capable of picking up bits of straw and paper. Similarly, glass rods and many other objects when they are rubbed with cloth, silk, or fur become electrified. Some substances become positively charged, whereas others become negatively charged; this classification depends on whether in the charged state they are attracted or repelled by charged amber, which is arbitrarily considered negative. The Greek word for amber is *elektron*.

This kind of electrification of objects was called static or frictional electricity, and for many years it was considered different from flowing electricity, which had been discovered by Luigi Galvani and by Alessandro Volta in the eighteenth century. Flowing electricity is the one we know commonly; it is easily made chemically from batteries and flows along wires. However, one of the accomplishments of the nineteenth century was to show that the two sorts of electricity are really the same. The experiments for this purpose involved the discovery and isolation of the fundamental unit of electricity—the electron.

Let us take a glass tube sealed at each end, with a metal plate inside each end connected by a wire to an outside source of current. Such a system is drawn in Figure 5. When the current is turned on, nothing happens in the tube. Normally the air in the tube offers such resistance to the passage of electricity that no current flows through it. If, however, the air has previously been sucked out of the tube so that the inside is almost a vacuum, the electricity can jump across the long gap in the tube, between the two terminal metal plates.

When the current jumps from one metal plate to the other, something actually passes through the gas in the tube; something flows in a stream from one end to the other. If a small glass plate coated with zinc sulfide is

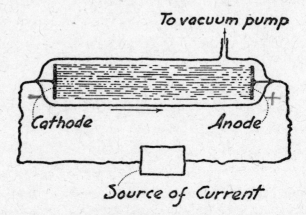

FIGURE 5. A GEISSLER TUBE

As the current is passed through the near vacuum in the tube, a stream of negative electrons passes from the negative cathode to the positive anode. The extremely dilute gas in the tube shows all sorts of pretty colors during the passage of the current.

placed in the path of the stream inside the tube, the zinc sulfide lights up the moment the current is turned on. If you look closely at the glowing plate of zinc sulfide, you can see that the glow is made up of tiny bursts of light all over it. It is as if now one particle of zinc sulfide is hit and bursts into a flash of light, then another particle of zinc sulfide is hit and bursts into light, then another, and another, and so on. The bursts of light are all the same size, a phenomenon that shows that the stream of electricity passing through the tube is composed of uniformly sized pieces, each of which when it hits a particle of zinc sulfide makes it give off a flash of light.

The stream that passes through the tube is made up not merely of units, but of negatively charged units. Their charge can be demonstrated by deflecting the stream with a magnet outside the tube. If the stream in the tube is narrow, it makes a glowing spot on the plate of zinc sulfide. As the magnet is brought near the tube the glowing spot shifts to the right or to the left depending on which way the magnet is held, and one can tell that the stream is negatively charged.

It was J. J. Thomson, the English physicist, who first showed that this stream is made up of charged unit particles, and he succeeded in weighing them. This sounds mysterious, but it is not. Just remember that it is easier to deflect a moving stream of ping-pong balls than a moving stream of freight cars. When a moving object is heavy it takes a lot of force to pull it out of its direct path, whereas if it is light, it can easily be pushed or pulled out of its motion in a straight line.

By measuring the magnetic force required to divert the stream of charged particles in the evacuated tube, J. J. Thomson was able to measure their mass. They turned out to be lighter by far than anything previously known. It will be recalled that the hydrogen atom is the lightest material particle. These charged units weigh only 1/1840 as much as a hydrogen atom.

As a result of this work we possess a new unit of matter, a particle that is 1840 times lighter than a hydrogen atom and that unlike the hydrogen atom carries a unit charge of electricity. In fact, Thomson was able to show that it *is* a unit charge of electricity. He called these new particles, electrons, and demonstrated that they are the electric current. Electricity is electrons, and when the current flows, electrons move.

All electrons are alike. In the drawing in Figure 5 the electrons come out of the metal plate on the left called the cathode, and travel to the metal plate on the right called the anode. It makes no difference what these metals are; the electrons that stream out from the negative cathode are all alike. They all weigh the same, and all have the same electrical charge.

Where are the electrons when the current does not flow through the evacuated tube? Where are the electrons in the battery when the wires are not connected? Where are the electrons when the generator is not turning in the powerhouse? These questions bring us right back to the structure of atoms. Clearly the electrons must be somewhere, since surely they are not created the moment the switch is closed in the lighting circuit. Where are they?

The electrons are in ordinary matter. Consider frictional electricity. The amber that has been rubbed with fur is negatively charged. This means that the amber has acquired electrons on its surface. These electrons can be led off the surface by a conducting wire and properly measured. They are the same electrons that form the stream in the evacuated tube and the current in the electric light. The amber acquired these electrons from the fur by rubbing them off the fur. As a result the amber became negative and the fur positive.

Evidently it is fairly easy to rub electrons off many materials. We do this every time we walk briskly on a carpet. The electrons are pulled off the carpet material and accumulate on the surface of the body. When we touch something metallic that can conduct the electrons from the surface of the body to the ever-receptive earth, they jump as a spark across the point of contact, and it is this concentration of electrons that causes the shock we feel on such occasions.

By various means electrons can be pulled out of all sorts of objects, no matter how innocent looking. Fur, carpets, copper, gold, cheese, salt, and even water yield electrons. Electrons can be boiled off a wire merely by heating it in a vacuum, as happens in every vacuum tube in a radio set. Some of these electrons must be near the surface of the matter from which they can be rubbed off so easily. And since all matter is made of atoms, some of the electrons must be near or on the surface of the atoms.

Ordinarily, objects are electrically neutral, and so are their atoms. When their surface electrons are pulled off, objects and their constituent atoms become positively charged, while the substance acquiring the electrons becomes negatively charged. It looks as if atoms in their normal or neutral condition are made of something positive, combined with electrons, which are negative. Atoms cannot be considered any longer as uniform homogeneous elastic balls. They have a structure; and at least the surface of this structure is concerned with the way in which atoms stick together to form molecules.

In the last section we learned that when two atoms are joined, each contributes something to the bonds that hold them together. Without going into the details of the experiments, we can say at once that what each atom contributes to the bond is an electron. The chemical bond that keeps atoms together consists of a pair of electrons, one from each atom, which the participating atoms hold in common. In this way a 1-bond atom (a monovalent atom) like hydrogen, or sodium, has 1 surface electron ready to be shared with another atom that is capable of reciprocal action.

The result is a 2-electron tie that keeps the atoms together. Elements that are divalent have 2 surface electrons that can be shared, and these can be reciprocally taken up by another divalent atom or by 2 monovalent atoms. And so on with trivalent atoms.

Water has the capacity of breaking some of these bonds in such a way that one of the atoms gives up its electron and becomes positive, while the other atom takes up the electron and becomes negative. Ordinary salt is sodium chloride and is written as NaCl, in which Na is the symbol for natrium or sodium. This is a neutral molecule as we all know who have eaten it all our lives. When sodium chloride is dissolved in water, the sodium loses an electron and become Na^+, which is positively charged, while the chlorine gains this electron and becomes negatively charged, Cl^-.

If now a current of electricity is sent through such a salt solution, Na^+ picks up a negative charge at the cathode or negative pole, and becomes a neutral sodium atom, which is deposited right there on the cathode. We can measure the number of electrons, that is, the amount of current, required to deposit a certain large number of sodium atoms at the cathode. Let us call this amount a Faraday of electricity. We can also measure the amount of current required to deposit that same number of copper atoms out of solution. The result is two Faradays of electricity. Thus it takes twice as many electrons to form a neutral copper atom as it did a sodium atom. In other words, in solution copper was Cu^{++} while sodium was Na^+. Copper is divalent, and sodium is monovalent. And this holds not only here but in all the chemical transformations that sodium and copper undergo. In the same way we find that aluminum, which is trivalent, requires three electrons to be neutralized and deposited out of solution. In solution it is therefore Al^{+++}. In short, valence means a labile surface electron ready to join an electron from another element to form a chemical bond.

A substance in the charged condition such as Na^+ or

Cu^{++} or Cl^- is often spoken of as ionized, and the individual charged atoms like Al^{+++} are called ions. The word *ion* means wanderer in Greek, and these charged atoms are so called because they can wander in an electric field.

Gone now is the simple billiard ball atom. In its place we have a sort of electrically neutral structure with easily detachable electrons on the surface. By the end of the nineteenth century this was all that was known for sure. However, during the last five years of the century there were ominous rumblings of future transformations in this simple structure that would eventually lead to the atomic bomb. These rumblings were the discoveries of x-rays and radioactivity.

3. RAYS FROM THE INTERIOR OF ATOMS

In describing the discovery of electrons I pictured what happens in an evacuated glass tube with sealed-in metal electrodes. Such tubes are tricky to make. The metal plates inside have to be connected with an outside source of electricity by means of wires that pass through the glass, and it is hard to make the joint of wire and glass airtight. In Germany there was an excellent glass blower, by the name of Heinrich Geissler, who learned the trick of sealing wires in a glass tube so that the seal remained tight even when the tube itself was almost completely exhausted of air. For this reason the tubes were known as Geissler tubes.

It was in such a Geissler tube that J. J. Thomson discovered electrons and measured their mass and charge. The stream of electrons in the Geissler tube could be made visible by their impact on a fluorescent zinc sulfide screen, and one could almost count the individual electron impacts as they produced bursts of light in the zinc sulfide particles of the screen.

The discharges through Geissler tubes are rather pretty, and served as items in the repertory of the physics professor to interest students and keep them awake. Many people had become familiar with them toward the end of the last century, but up to 1895 all attention had been concentrated on the effects produced inside the tube by the stream of electrons, or cathode rays, as they were then called. One looked at the glass, or at the anode plate, or at the fluorescent screen near the anode.

It was in 1895 that the German physicist Wilhelm K. Roentgen discovered that something comes off the anode through the glass and is scattered all around it. He found this phenomenon because he noticed that even when the Geissler tube was completely covered by black paper, a fluorescent zinc sulfide screen held outside near the Geissler tube in the dark glowed when the tube was discharged. Roentgen observed that the fluorescence was strongest just near the anode, and he concluded that something was given off by the anode that could penetrate glass and paper and affect the zinc sulfide.

Roentgen called the things that were given off x-rays because they acted like rays of light, but were not light, and their nature was unknown. They were not electrons because electrons cannot pass through glass or paper, and these passed easily through both.

We know now that x-rays are really much like rays of light, but of shorter wavelength, and of more power and energy. Ordinary light is made up of a series of waves. So are x-rays. The difference is that the x-ray waves are extremely small in comparison. The precise wavelength depends on the voltage of the current going through the Geissler tube. Because of their small size and great energy, x-rays have enormous penetrating power.

One hardly needs to spend time describing x-rays, because almost everybody knows about them these days. From the plaything of the physicists, they have become the great tools of medical diagnosis and treatment. The types, sizes, shapes, and powers of x-ray tubes depend upon the purposes for which they are needed, from the small model used by the dentist to the enormously powerful instruments used in the treatment of cancer.

For our present story, x-rays are important because they demand an explanation. Evidently they are emitted from the metal of the anode when it is struck by the electrons in the Geissler tube. What produces them, and where do they come from? They must come from the atoms of the metal when these are hit by electrons in motion. But how and why? Before it was possible to formulate an answer, the scientific world was presented

with an even greater mystery by the discovery of radioactivity.

4. ENERGY FROM THE INTERIOR OF ATOMS

Roentgen had discovered x-rays by the glow or fluorescence of a zinc sulfide screen. Many other substances
beside zinc sulfide fluoresce, and the properties and
classification of such materials was a specialty of the
physicist Henri Becquerel. In fact, it had been a specialty
of his father before him.

Some minerals when quickly brought into the dark
after exposure to the sun can be seen to glow for some
time afterward. The luminous dial of a watch contains
such a fluorescent substance. If it is exposed to a strong
light and then taken into the dark, it will glow very
brightly at first and then gradually fade. Experiments
showed that sunlight was most effective in producing
fluorescence, and that it was the invisible ultraviolet light
that actually did the work. The minerals absorb the invisible ultraviolet light and emit ordinary visible light at
once and later.

One story has it that Becquerel wondered whether, in
addition to the ordinary visible light that they emit on
exposure to the sun, such minerals may not also produce
invisible light and perhaps even more penetrating rays,
like those just discovered by Roentgen. He therefore
placed some of the minerals in a tray on top of a carefully

wrapped photographic plate, and exposed the arrangement to the sunlight. His idea was that if invisible or active rays were emitted as fluorescence they would penetrate the black paper and fog the photographic plate. And sure enough, the plate did show considerable fogging with some of the minerals.

However, this was not the end. The story continues that the sun did not shine every day in that winter of 1896 in Paris, and Becquerel, after setting up the mineral in the tray on the wrapped photographic plate, placed the whole preparation in a drawer in his laboratory to wait for the sun. The sun did not shine for a few days, and he therefore used the photographic plate for some other purpose. On developing it, he was astonished to find it badly fogged much as if it had been under the fluorescent mineral that was being exposed to sunlight. Evidently even in the dark and without previous exposure to sunlight, the mineral had given off some rays that had passed right through the paper and affected the photographic plate.

A survey showed that a number of minerals had this strange property. Further study revealed that only those minerals that contained the element uranium were capable of spontaneously giving off this invisible penetrating radiation, and that the extent of fogging the photographic plate was proportional to the uranium content of the mineral. Becquerel called these minerals "radioactive" because of their capacity to give off this extraordinary radiation.

One of Becquerel's colleagues was Pierre Curie, who with his wife Marie became interested in these phenomena. Becquerel suggested that Marie Curie study for this penetrating radiation as large a variety of minerals as possible. In so doing, she found that there was one other element in addition to uranium that could produce radioactivity. This element was thorium, and Marie Curie and her husband Pierre were soon able to show that the capacity to fog a photographic plate in the dark was proportional to the uranium or thorium content of the mineral, depending on which it contained.

With one exception. This was the black mineral pitchblende, which though it contained uranium, showed a radioactivity much more powerful than could be accounted for by its uranium content. The Curies suspected that there might be still another radioactive element besides uranium and thorium. If this were true, the unknown element would have to be much more powerful than uranium, because pitchblende is mostly uranium, and only a trifling percentage of this unknown and undetected element would have to be responsible for the exceptional power of pitchblende to blacken a photographic plate kept in the dark.

The rest of this tale is not for us to tell here; it has already been reported in books, movies, and the press, and has become common knowledge of our time. The Curies worked at the problem for a number of years and by their efforts discovered the new element that they had suspected. That new element was radium.

Radium and radioactivity were not easily assimilated by physicists at the end of the nineteenth century. Henry Adams records that S. P. Langley, the physicist of the Smithsonian Institution, was deeply troubled as he looked at the radium and radioactivity demonstration at the Paris Exposition of 1900. Here are elements that without any outside supply of energy keep on steadily emitting powerful and penetrating rays of enormous energy content. Where do these rays come from? Clearly they must come from the atoms of uranium, thorium, and radium. But if so, what sort of structures can these atoms be? Certainly they cannot be the old homogeneous balls; they must have structures deep inside that can emit these rays of enormous energy without themselves changing perceptibly.

5. FRAGMENTS FROM THE INTERIOR OF ATOMS

With the study of radium and radioactivity we enter the twentieth century. Much of the chemical work on radium and its related compounds was done by Pierre and Marie Curie, and for that they were awarded the Nobel prize in 1903. However, it is the physical aspects of radioactivity that are of interest in the development of our story. These investigations were made by a number of people, but especially by Ernest Rutherford, who worked in Manchester, and later in Cambridge, England.

The basic phenomenon is that a covered photographic

plate held near radium becomes blackened on subsequent development, as if it had been struck by light. Similarly a glass plate covered with zinc sulfide glows when it is brought near radium in the dark. This principle is used in making luminous dials on watches. Radium paint is zinc sulfide plus a trace of radium, which keeps the zinc sulfide aglow. A zinc sulfide plate and a photographic plate are two devices used in exploring the nature of what is given off by radium.

Figure 6 illustrates the kind of experiments that were made for this purpose. Radium has to be kept in lead containers, because what it gives off is injurious to life.

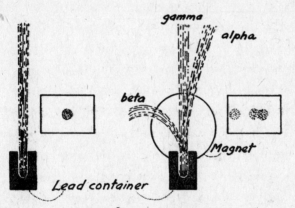

FIGURE 6. RAYS FROM RADIUM

In the drawing to the left, all the rays leave the container in one beam, which shows as a glowing circular spot on the plate of zinc sulfide. In the drawing to the right, a magnet is held perpendicular to the plane of the page. At once the beam breaks into three parts: the alpha beam to the right, the beta to the left, and the undeflected gamma beam straight ahead. These are shown as three glowing circles on the zinc sulfide plate.

Imagine a long and narrow tube of lead with one end sealed, and with a few grains of radium at the bottom. The reason for the long narrow tube is that whatever is given off by the radium has to travel along the length of the tube, and will come out in a narrow beam traveling in a straight line. One can explore the shape and character of this beam by placing a photographic plate at different distances from the opening and seeing what size spots are produced. Easier still is using a zinc sulfide screen. Placed near the opening of the lead tube, the screen glows in a small circle the diameter of the opening. As the screen is moved away from the opening the circle increases very slightly, which shows that the beam is straight and well defined, but very slightly divergent.

Now bring a strong magnet near the beam, and observe what happens to the fluorescent circle. It is still there, but it has become distinctly weaker. This change means that there is still a beam that goes straight out, undeflected as before, but it has become less intense. By exploring with our fluorescent screen the region around the opening we can find out what has happened to weaken our beam. Instead of one circular spot, we can now find three, the central one and one on each side. Remove the magnet, and all three jump together to form the undeviated central beam; return the magnet and the beam splits into three. Evidently, at least three different rays are given off by the radium. Rutherford called these "alpha," "beta," and "gamma" rays.

Further examination revealed the nature of the three kinds of rays. The alpha ray was deflected by the magnet in such a way as to show that it was positively charged. Moreover, it was only slightly deflected even by a powerful magnet. Therefore, it was probably composed of relatively heavy, charged particles. These were named alpha particles.

Toward the other side of the undeflected beam was the beta ray. It was easily deflected by the magnet in such a way as to show that it was negatively charged. Moreover, it was deflected much more than the alpha beam; therefore its negatively charged particles were much lighter than the alpha particles. These negative beta particles were easy to identify: they were electrons, the same kind of electrons that are found on charged amber and in the evacuated Geissler tubes.

Finally the undeflected gamma beam turned out to be x-rays. These are not charged particles, but are the same kind of rays that come out from the anode of the Geissler tube and pass through the glass.

Of the three things emitted by radium, two turned out to be old friends, electrons and x-rays. The alpha particles, however, were something new. Measurements by Rutherford and others showed that the weight of these particles is about 4 times that of a hydrogen atom and that the velocities with which they move is of the order of 1/10 the speed of light. What are they? The inert gas helium has an atomic weight of 4, which means that its atom weighs 4 times as much as a hydrogen atom. One might therefore guess the identity of an alpha particle. But please remember that helium is a noble gas and was not well known in 1900. It was not until later that the alpha particle was shown to be an ionized helium atom, an atom of helium from which two electrons had been stripped off, and which is therefore He^{++}.

In addition to these three rays, it was soon found that around radium or minerals containing radium the air becomes a good conductor of electricity. A conductor of electricity is something that permits electricity to go from one spot to another. This passage of electricity takes place when the intervening atoms become charged or ionized. Something was being given off that ionized the air around the radium. And furthermore, a certain amount of heat was steadily generated.

Radium gives off all these things all the time. And no outside influence—not light nor heat nor electricity—has any effect on the rate with which radium emits these radiations and particles. These emissions from radium involve the release of tremendous energies. An alpha particle travels very fast indeed and therefore has lots of energy. The beta particles, which are electrons, also travel fast. Since they are so much smaller than alpha particles they do not involve so much energy, but there is energy aplenty. And then there are the x-rays and the heat.

All this goes on indefinitely, day in and day out, year in and year out. The energy that drives out these electrons and alpha particles and gamma rays and heat must come from somewhere. The alpha particles and the electrons themselves must also come from somewhere. They can come only from the interior of the atom, not from its surface. The rearrangement of atoms in molecules could never yield energies or particles of this magnitude. Heretofore all the energies that were known came from the changing of the bonds between atoms in the molecules of compounds. These were the chemical energies that served for fire, fuel, and explosives. With radioactivity, energies were being released that were of a totally different order of magnitude from those furnished by chemical transformations.

For example, measurements even on minute amounts of radium showed that if one ounce of radium were to deliver all the x-rays, alpha particles, and electrons of which it is capable, the energy would be equivalent to the heat supplied by 10 tons of coal. Ten tons of coal are roughly 32,000 ounces, which means that weight for weight radium can yield 32,000 times as much energy as coal.

Such measurements and computations were made very early in the century. Moreover, the energy released was always spoken of as atomic energy. It is well to keep this in mind as an antidote to the all too prevalent notion that atomic energy was suddenly discovered as a great secret the day before yesterday by the Manhattan District. To scientists atomic energy is an old story.

III

THE ATOM DEVELOPS A STRUCTURE

1. THE ATOM HAS A NUCLEUS

During its existence radium continues to emit alpha particles, which we found to be helium stripped of two electrons. What is left of the radium after it has given off these alpha particles? The answer came when it was observed that around the radium there accumulates a strange gas. This gas was called radium emanation because no one quite knew what it was. Later its properties were studied, and we now know that it is a gas like neon and krypton, a member of the group of noble gases, which are in the terminal column of the Periodic Table. When its identity became established radium emanation was named radon, a combination of the first and last few letters of its original designation.

What should this gas be? Marie Curie found that the atomic weight of radium is nearly 226. If each radium atom emits an alpha particle that has an atomic weight of 4, and if what is left becomes the gas radon, then it should have an atomic weight of 222. It took some time to accumulate enough radon gas for the British chemist

William Ramsay to determine its atomic weight. And it was exciting to learn that its atomic weight is really 222. This information tells us either that helium is suddenly created out of radium, or more likely, that the atom of radium is an arrangement from which the helium particle can be easily formed or detached. In either case the radium atom must have a structure of some complexity.

It was Rutherford who performed the experiments that defined this structure. The alpha particle turned out to be most useful in these experiments because it was a particle with 2 positive charges and a mass of 4 that could be sent in a stream moving with great velocities. In air such a stream of alpha particles, as it issues from radium, goes about 5 or 6 inches before it is dissipated by contact with the millions of atoms that it meets. Rutherford directed the alpha particles close against a thin piece of gold leaf and by means of the fluorescent zinc sulfide screen he watched what happened to the beam of particles.

Three things occurred, which are shown in the diagram of Figure 7. First, most of the alpha particles by far breezed right through the gold leaf as if it were not there. This seemed to show that so far as the alpha particle is concerned, gold leaf is mostly empty space. Second, some of the alpha particles were slightly deflected from their straight path. And third, an occasional alpha particle bounced back or was sharply deflected as if it had hit something its own size. The relative infrequency of such a direct collision emphasizes the fact that the gold leaf is mainly vacant space. Considering that the alpha particle is a helium atom, that gold is a solid with its atoms packed close together, and that gold is a relatively heavy atom, this emptiness of the gold leaf is much greater than

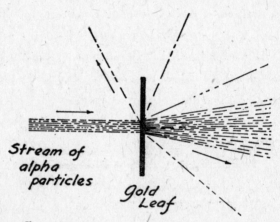

Stream of alpha particles

Gold Leaf

FIGURE 7. STREAM OF ALPHA PARTICLES THROUGH GOLD LEAF

Note that whereas most of the particles go straight through some are slightly deflected and others are bounced back at sharp angles as if they had hit something hard.

can be accounted for by the comparatively small spaces between the gold atoms. It must be that the gold atom itself contains a lot of empty space.

Once this was recognized it became necessary to devise a new picture of the atom, a picture that would account for not only all the old chemical knowledge but the new radioactivity information as well. It was Rutherford who supplied this new picture. He suggested that the atom is made of two parts—a tiny central nucleus in which most of the mass is concentrated, and the rest of the atom, with a diameter about 10,000 times as large as the nucleus. This region around the nucleus is space containing electrons. Electrons are negative, and since the atom as a whole is neutral, the nucleus must be positive.

In these terms an alpha particle is really only the tiny nucleus of a helium atom, because its two electrons have been stripped off. Since it is so minute, it can sweep through gold leaf without meeting anything. Mostly it goes through the empty region around the nucleus of the gold atom. This idea also explains why every once in a while when an alpha particle hits the nucleus of a gold atom it bounces back or is sharply deflected. The reason is that the gold nucleus is positively charged and the alpha particle is positively charged and they both contain the major mass of the atom. They are both tiny and therefore meet only rarely; but when they do collide the result is a really massive encounter, which sets the lighter alpha particle bouncing back across space. Finally, the idea explains the relative ease with which electrons can be stripped from atoms. The electrons are in the large space surrounding the nucleus. Some of them are undoubtedly near the surface of this space where they are available to form bonds in chemical reactions, and these surface electrons can be easily removed.

2. THE ATOM IS ELECTRICALLY BALANCED

How many electrons are there in this relatively large space surrounding the tiny nucleus of the atom? That depends. Hydrogen is the lightest atom, and one can easily strip an electron from it and leave a hydrogen ion H^+ with one positive charge on it. Moreover it has never been possible to remove any more than this single electron from hydrogen.

Perhaps there is only one electron in hydrogen. Let us suppose so for a moment. Then the hydrogen atom whose weight is 1 would be made up (a) of a nucleus whose weight is also 1 with a single positive charge on it, and (b) of one electron with its mass of 1/1840 and its single negative charge roaming in the space around the nucleus.

Helium is the next element in order, with an atomic weight of 4. It is relatively easy to strip one electron from helium, and not too difficult to remove a second electron as well, leaving ionized He^{++}. These are the alpha particles that come roaring out of radium with velocities of 18,000 miles per second; but similar particles can be produced in the laboratory by sending an electric current through a Geissler tube with a little helium in it. Since no more electrons can be pulled out, it seems entirely possible that the helium atom really has only two electrons in the space around the nucleus. The nucleus would then be left with a mass of 4 and with two positive charges on it to balance the two negative electrons around it.

Is it possible that the third element, lithium, has 3 electrons; the fourth element, beryllium, 4 electrons; the fifth, boron, 5 electrons; and so on to uranium, which might have 92 electrons? It is not only possible; it is even true. The evidence for this regular augmentation in the number of electrons as one goes from one element to the next in the Periodic Table is varied and plentiful. Some of it is amusing, and shows how work in one field, even if only by analogy, can enrich the knowledge of another field.

When a beam of sunlight enters a darkened room with dust in it, one can see the beam of light clearly defined as the light is scattered from the dust particles. The more dust particles in the room the more the light is scattered; and if there is a real cloud of dust, the light is scattered so much that one can hardly see beyond it. The same thing happens to the beams from the headlights of a car in a fog. The small particles of water making up the fog in the air scatter the light that shines on them. The denser the fog the more the light is scattered, the less of it gets through the fog, and the less one can see through a fog with even the most powerful beam of light. By measuring the fraction of the incident light that goes straight through the fog and the fraction that is scattered by the fog particles, one can estimate the number of water droplets in the fog—or the number of dust particles in the air. This method is accurate for determining the number of fine particles in a cloudy suspension in air or in water and is used frequently in analytical chemistry.

A similar method can be used to determine the number of electrons in the space around the nucleus of atoms. Just think of electrons as small particles forming a suspension around the nucleus. In solid materials, the atoms are rather close to one another, and the electrons form an almost continuous suspension throughout the substance, with an occasional nucleus here and there. Now imagine a beam of light shining through this suspension of electrons. If there are few electrons, only a little light will be scattered by them, and most of it will go right through. But if there are many electrons, much light will be scattered, and only a small fraction of it will get through the material.

Naturally a beam of ordinary light is too coarse for this job. Its wave is so large that it passes over a tiny electron without being in the least affected, much as a huge wave on the ocean washes over a man without being the slightest bit altered in appearance or direction. What we need for the electron suspension is light with a very small wave. Such are x-rays, whose wavelength is about ten thousand times smaller than that of ordinary light. When x-ray scattering measurements are made with thin layers of the various elements in the Periodic Table, it turns out that each successive element in order of its atomic number acts as if it has 1 more electron in the space around the nucleus.

Since hydrogen has 1 electron, and helium 2, lithium must have 3, beryllium 4, boron 5, carbon 6, and so on up to uranium, which has 92. The atomic number, that is the numerical position of an element in the atomic series, gives the number of electrons surrounding the central nucleus of its atom. Notice also that the atomic number places an element in a specific spot in the Periodic Table, and since a specific spot means certain definite chemical properties it follows that the chemical characteristics of an element are determined by the number of electrons surrounding its nucleus. This is an important fact to remember.

The electrons are negative charges. The atom as a whole, however, is neutral. Therefore the nucleus must possess a like number of positive charges to balance the number of electrons around it. One need not accept this on faith, because there are many independent proofs for it. I will consider one kind of evidence because it follows so simply from the gold-foil experiment described in the preceding section.

The manner in which a stream of alpha particles behaves as it passes through a foil of metal must depend on the charge on the nucleus of the metal. An alpha particle is the positively charged helium nucleus. If it comes near the positively charged nucleus of another atom the alpha particle will be repelled, because like charges repel each other. The extent of repulsion will depend on the charge on the metal nucleus. A large positive charge will repel the alpha particle more than will a small one.

A stream of alpha particles passing through a foil of metal will therefore be scattered to an extent depending on the charge on its nucleus. The higher the atomic number of the metal the more the beam of alpha particles will be scattered, and the precise degree of scattering can be used to determine the charge on the nucleus.

Experiments made on thin foils of many elements bore this reasoning out fully. The scatter in the beam as it passed through various foils behaved as if each successive element in the Periodic Table has one more positive charge on its nucleus than the one preceding it. Again it looks as if the atomic number represents not only the number of electrons but also the number of positive charges on the nucleus of an atom. The two sets of opposite charges balance each other and the result is a neutral atom.

3. THE ATOMIC NUCLEUS PRESENTS DETAILS

We now have an atom composed of a central nucleus surrounded by electrons in a space thousands of times larger than the nucleus. The atomic number, that is the serial number of the element in the Periodic Table, determines the number of electrons as well as the number of balancing positive charges on the nucleus. The atomic weight is essentially the weight of the nucleus, because the electrons weigh so little.

Electrons we know about. They are units of negative electricity and have a mass of only 1/1840 of a hydrogen atom. But what is the nucleus, and how are the positive charges and the mass distributed in it? Again it was Rutherford who furnished the answers by experiment and thought.

Rutherford attempted to break up the nuclei of a variety of substances by bombarding them with streams of alpha particles which he could get from radium. He first tried hydrogen gas and watched particularly for those rare times when there was a collision between an alpha particle and something in the hydrogen gas. Even more than in the gold leaf the alpha particle went straight ahead most of the time. But when an alpha particle did hit a hydrogen nucleus it sent it careening. The reason is clear. An alpha particle is four times as heavy as a hydrogen nucleus and is traveling 18,000 miles a second; and when it meets the hydrogen nucleus head on, the impact is a powerful one. However, in spite of this powerful impact, nothing comes out except a positively charged hydrogen nucleus.

Rutherford then tried bombarding nitrogen gas with alpha particles. The frequency of collision was somewhat greater, but spinning out as the result of the collision there again appeared a hydrogen nucleus. He then directed a stream of alpha particles into sodium vapor, and again only the same positively charged hydrogen nucleus appeared as the result of a collision. Nothing smaller or different appeared from other elements similarly exposed to streams of alpha particles. In short, it looked as if the charged hydrogen ion, H^+, is the unit of nuclear structure.

The charged hydrogen nucleus became so common that it was given a special name. H^+ is called a proton. It has a mass of 1 and a positive charge of 1. Since nothing else was known to come out of the nucleus it was considered as the unit building block out of which all atomic nuclei are constructed.

This picture of the nucleus raises a pretty question. The atomic number of hydrogen is 1. Therefore its nucleus is a single proton of weight 1 and positive charge 1, and it has 1 electron around it. But consider helium, which has an atomic number of 2. Its atom contains 2 electrons, which are balanced by 2 positive charges on the nucleus. Two positive charges mean 2 protons. But 2 protons weigh only 2 atomic units, and the atomic weight of helium is 4. Where does the additional mass of 2 come from?

The same problem arises for all succeeding elements. Lithium has an atomic number of 3. Hence its nuclear charge is 3, and therefore its nucleus has 3 protons. But its atomic weight is 7, so that 4 units of mass have to be accounted for. Or consider carbon, whose atomic number is 6. Its nucleus has 6 protons. But 6 protons weigh only

6 units, and the atomic weight of carbon is 12. This situation continues to be true, so that the atomic weight of an element beyond hydrogen is about twice as large as its atomic number, and for the heavier elements much more than twice. Thus the atomic number of silver is 47,

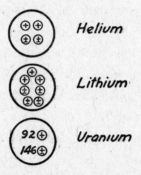

FIGURE 8. SAMPLE ATOMIC NUCLEI

The nuclei of three elements as they were pictured in the years before 1932. Each nucleus contains several protons (+) and several proton-electron combinations (±).

while its atomic weight is 108; the atomic number of lead is 82, and its atomic weight is 207; the atomic number of uranium is 92, and its atomic weight is 238. What makes up the extra weight of the nucleus?

For about twenty years no one knew the real answer to this puzzle. In the meanwhile one relied on the fact that until then the only particle that had been forced out of the nucleus was the proton. The suggestion was therefore commonly made that the nucleus is really composed of the number of protons corresponding to the atomic *weight*, but that the positive charges in excess of those required by the atomic number are neutralized by a like number of electrons *within* the nucleus.

With the aid of the pictures in Figure 8 we can work this idea out for a few cases. For example, helium really has 4 protons in the nucleus to give it the mass of 4. But 2 of them are combined with 1 electron each to form 2 neutralized groups, so that the net charge on the nucleus is only 2 positive units. Lithium with an atomic weight of 7 and an atomic number of 3 behaves similarly. It has 7 protons in its nucleus, but of these, 4 are neutralized by 1 electron each *inside* the nucleus leaving a net positive charge of 3, which in turn is balanced by the 3 electrons outside the nucleus.

In this way one can proceed to the higher elements, as for example, uranium, whose atomic number is 92, and whose atomic weight is 238. This statement means that outside the nucleus it has 92 negative electrons, which determine its chemical properties. Its nucleus contains 238 protons, of which 146 are neutralized by an electron each inside the nucleus, leaving a net positive charge of 92 to balance the 92 outside electrons.

This explanation seemed fairly reasonable, but nobody felt comfortable with it. It accounted formally for the facts, but no one was happy with neutralized pairs of protons and electrons inside the nucleus. They left too many questions unanswered.

Such was the situation in 1912 and the problem remained in this state until 1932. In the interval, other events took place that revealed and clarified other aspects of the structure of the atom.

4. THE ATOM IS A SOLAR SYSTEM

The years that followed the establishment of the nuclear atom saw the development of two lines of experimentation. One was concerned with the arrangements of the electrons around the nucleus, while the other was devoted to exploring the interior of the nucleus. Strictly, the path of our story from atom to atomic bomb goes through the nucleus only, and any time we spend on the surrounding electrons is a diversion. However, for the sake of completeness I propose to devote this section to the electrons. The nucleus is not the whole atom, and if the reader has gone with me so far, he is probably interested in the whole structure. The work on the electrons around the nucleus grew by virtue of ideas developed by Niels Bohr in 1912 almost immediately after Rutherford had originated the nuclear atom.

The space in the atom outside the nucleus is enormous compared with the size of the nucleus, or with the much smaller size of an electron. In the atom of hydrogen the single electron is near the outer rim of the atom. If its nucleus were enlarged to the size of a baseball, its electron would be a speck about eight city blocks away. Actually, of course, this atomic distance is small. The diameter of a hydrogen atom is nearly 1/200,000,000 of an inch; in other words, 200,000,000 hydrogen atoms could be placed one next the other in an inch. Relative to the nucleus or to the electron, however, the atomic space is prodigious.

It is in this circumnuclear space that the electrons are to be found. Obviously, they cannot be there just helter-skelter. When there is so much regularity in the Periodic Table, it is hardly to be expected that the electrons are merely dumped into this outside region without being arranged in some definite system. The whole of chemistry depends on the behavior of some of these electrons because of the way some of them are shared to form the chemical bonds that unite atoms into molecules. Moreover, each element in the Periodic Table has one more electron than its preceding neighbor. Surely the electrons are distributed with some regularity.

Let us look at the Periodic Table (p. 27) in the vertical column under lithium. It contains the soft alkali metals, lithium, sodium, potassium, rubidium, and cesium, with which we are already acquainted. Hydrogen can be in two columns, and may be included in the present one. All these elements are monovalent: they have 1 chemical bond. Being monovalent means that they each have 1 electron on the surface, which can easily be shared with another element.

Hydrogen is monovalent because it has only 1 electron. But lithium has 3 electrons; yet 1 of them acts as if it were on the surface, easily available. Similarly, sodium has 11 electrons and yet 1 is on the surface for valence purposes. And so on with potassium, which has 19 electrons, 1 of which is a valence electron; rubidium with a total of 37 electrons, and cesium with 55 electrons, each with 1 valence electron on the surface of the atom.

It almost looks as if the electrons were arranged in shells, and each time we come around the Periodic Table to the column of alkali metals, a new shell of electrons gets started with the one electron in it. It is this single electron in the new outer shell that is easily available, and that makes these elements similar chemically.

If this idea of shells of electrons is right, then the element that just precedes one of these soft alkali metals should have a complete and stable shell of electrons. Moreover, since the electron shell is complete and stable, there should be no easily detachable electrons, the element should have no valence electrons, and therefore it should be an inert substance, which does not combine with other substances.

Now look at the Periodic Table and see what precedes lithium. Helium does; and helium is an inert gas, one of the noble series. Moreover, neon precedes sodium; argon precedes potassium; krypton precedes rubidium; and xenon precedes cesium. In each case the preceding element is a stable inert gas, which enters into no chemical combinations. These inert gases are all in the same column. It must be that they have nothing but complete or stable electron shells around the nucleus.

In this way we learn that the first completed electron shell contains 2 electrons and is represented by helium; the second completed shell contains 8 electrons, and corresponds to neon with its total of 10 electrons. Similarly the third shell also has 8 electrons, making a total of 18 electrons in the three shells, and this represents argon. Krypton with its 36 electrons then has four shells of electrons: the first contains 2, the second 8, the third has been enlarged to 18, and the last contains 8 again as did the outer shells of neon and argon. Then xenon with its 54 electrons has its fourth shell enlarged to have 18 electrons and its outer fifth shell has 8 electrons as did neon, argon, and krypton. Finally radon, with its 86 electrons, also has 8 electrons in its outer sixth shell. These are shown in the drawings in Figure 9 as diagrams for illustration. Eight electrons in the outer shell seems a stable and symmetrical number.

The idea of electron shells is so good that by following it out logically one finds the most illuminating information about atoms and their positions in the Periodic Table. If the elements in the helium column represent completed or stable electron shells, and the elements in the lithium column represent the first electron in a new shell, then the elements in the beryllium column next to it should represent 2 electrons in the new shell. These 2 electrons in the new outer shell are obviously free to be shared, which means that the elements in the beryllium column should have 2 chemical bonds and be divalent. They are.

Calcium combines with oxygen, which we know to be divalent, to form lime or calcium oxide, CaO. So does magnesium, and so does barium, and so do beryllium,

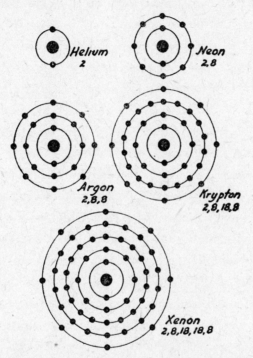

FIGURE 9. ELECTRON SHELLS IN THE NOBLE GASES

For helium, 2 electrons make the first completed shell. Each of the other noble gases has 8 electrons in the outer shell, while the inner shells are completely saturated with electrons.

strontium, and radium combine with one atom of oxygen to form stable oxides.

It is equally revealing to examine the elements that just precede the inert noble gases with their stable outer shells. Fluorine precedes neon. Neon has one completed shell of 2 and a second of 8 electrons. Therefore fluorine with its 9 electrons has the first completed shell of 2; but its second shell has only 7 electrons, just lacking 1 of completion. It should be particularly easy for fluorine to share 1 electron with another element that has an easy one to supply. Thus fluorine should have a great tendency to combine with elements like sodium and calcium, which have only 1 and 2 electrons in the outermost shell. This tendency, of course, is true of the whole group of elements in the fluorine column. Chlorine, bromine, and iodine all combine easily with sodium, lithium, and potassium to form salts like NaCl (sodium chloride) and LiCl (lithium chloride), since each element is monovalent. Also they combine with calcium and magnesium to form $CaCl_2$ (calcium chloride) and $MgCl_2$ (magnesium chloride), since both calcium and magnesium are divalent. This kind of reaction tells us that fluorine, chlorine, and the others in the same column have all their electron shells completed or stable except for 1 electron in the very outermost shell. The same is true of hydrogen, which has 1 electron. It may be considered as having 1 electron more than nothing, or 1 less than the complete shell of 2 that helium has.

If we had the space we could examine many other properties of the elements and find with what astonishing niceness they are predictable from the idea of a series of electron shells surrounding the nucleus. I cannot resist describing just one more property, because it fits in with information that we already know.

Earlier I described how atoms can become electrically charged, and be ions or wanderers in an electrical field. Since the alkali metals, lithium, sodium, and so on in the same column of the Periodic Table, each have only one electron in a newly formed outer shell, it should be relatively easy to pull this electron off and leave the element electrically unbalanced. Normally the number of positive charges on the nucleus equals the number of negative electrons around the nucleus. If one of these electrons is stripped off, the atom will be left with 1 extra positive charge and become a positive ion. This is true; the alkali metals do easily form ions like Li^+ (lithium ion), Na^+ (sodium ion), K^+ (potassium ion) and so on, each with one charge.

What is more, the elements in the beryllium column should form divalent ions. Their 2 electrons should be easily removable; not so easily as the 1 in the preceding alkali metals, but still fairly easily. This is also true; calcium forms the ion Ca^{++}; magnesium forms the ion Mg^{++}, and so on with the others, each with its 2 positive charges.

Finally the elements in the boron column should have 3 electrons in the last shell, and when these are stripped off, the ions should have 3 positive charges. And so they do: aluminum forms Al^{+++}, boron forms B^{+++}, and so on.

Now consider fluorine, chlorine, and the other elements in that column. They lack 1 electron to complete a stable outer electron shell of 8 electrons. This means that 1 electron can easily slip in, and the atom will have 1 more

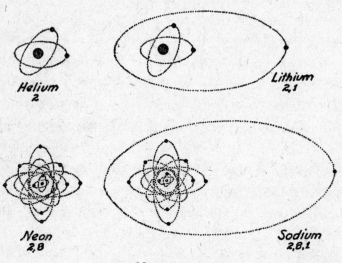

FIGURE 10. ELECTRON ORBITS

A fanciful picture of the paths followed by electrons. Notice helium and neon with their completed shells; and lithium and sodium each with 1 electron in a new shell.

electron than the number of positive charges on the nucleus. It will be negatively charged, and will become a negative ion. Thus fluorine becomes F^-, chlorine Cl^-, and iodine I^-, each with a single negative charge.

In Figure 9 the electron shells have been drawn as circles. Obviously this is because the paper is flat; in reality the shells must be spheres and tridimensional. This is a good first approximation, like assuming that the planets go around the sun in circles. Actually they go in ellipses, and similarly the electron shells are most probably ellipsoids. A fanciful way in which the electrons may be arranged is shown in Figure 10, especially if one assumes that the electrons move around the nucleus, as indeed one must.

The electron-shell arrangement of the circumnuclear electrons is one of the most beautiful ideas in science. The precise positions and movements of all the electrons have been worked out in fair detail, and some of the correspondences that have been first predicted and later discovered are startling in their subtlety. In particular those concerned with the colors produced by the elements under various conditions have been studied most rigorously and represent thinking and imagination of the highest order.

However, this is not our direction now. Alluring as this field is, we must leave it, and return to the interior of the nucleus to follow the development of its structure as it leads to the disconcerting realities of the atomic bomb.

IV

ATOMIC STRUCTURE IS COMPLETED

1. ISOTOPES: ATOMS DIFFERENT INSIDE BUT IDENTICAL OUTSIDE

Atoms are made of protons and electrons. A proton weighs 1 unit, and an electron 1/1840 or 0.00054 unit. Since the electron weighs so trifling an amount, why then are the atomic weights of the elements not whole or very nearly whole numbers?

The problem is an old one. Early in the nineteenth century after Dalton had suggested the atomic theory, Prout had proposed that all atoms were made up of hydrogen. Prout's hypothesis had to be discarded because the atomic weights of the elements were not exact multiples of the weight of hydrogen. This is not a matter of just ordinary accuracy. By 1900, atomic weights had been measured with a precision greater than any other constant of chemistry and were known to the fourth and fifth decimal places. They certainly were not whole numbers, nor were they multiples of hydrogen. Prout's hypothesis had long been abandoned, and yet here we are adopting essentially the same idea, by assuming that all atoms are made up of protons and electrons. If our theory of atomic structure is correct, why indeed are atomic weights not whole numbers?

Fortunately, this question did not bother investigators for very long, because by the time Rutherford had established the nuclear structure of the atom, other phenomena had already suggested the answer. The reason that atomic weights are not whole numbers is that the elements as usually isolated and purified chemically are not single elements, but mixtures. This statement needs to be explained and justified.

Take the element ionium. In 1906 this was a new element, which had just been discovered by B. B. Boltwood at Yale. He had isolated it from pitchblende, the mineral that contains a lot of uranium, and from which the Curies several years before had extracted radium and startled the world. Further study showed that the chemical properties of ionium were very much like those of thorium. It had the same appearance, the same solubilities, the same melting point, and even the same color characteristics as thorium. Yet the two differed in atomic weight. The atomic weight of ionium is 231.5; that of thorium is 232.1.

Direct comparison of ionium and thorium made certain that the two were not merely similar chemically; they were identical. If the two were mixed it became impossible to separate them. Separation is largely a chemical procedure depending on differences between substances in solubility, boiling point, or combining capacity. When two different substances are dissolved in one solution, the addition of another liquid may well precipitate one substance while the other remains in solution. But thorium and ionium have identical chemical properties and cannot be separated. Yet they cannot be the same because their atomic weights are different.

True, the difference in atomic weight is only 0.6, and seems small. However, the very fact that atomic weights can be determined with great precision to several decimal places makes a difference of 0.6 as certain and real as anything can be. Here, therefore, are two substances with the same chemical properties but different atomic weights.

This is indeed a riddle. But in this case the riddles came in pairs. It will be recalled that radium spontaneously gives off alpha particles, electrons, and gamma rays, and leaves radium emanation or radon. Radon is itself radioactive, and in a little while breaks down to radium-A, which is also radioactive and leaves radium-B, which breaks down to radium-C, and so on through several transformations ending in a substance that is stable and that looks like lead. It has not only the same appearance, but the same chemical properties, the same color characteristics, and all the common attributes of lead. If it is mixed with ordinary lead, the two cannot be separated from the mixture. Yet the two have different origins.

What adds to the puzzle is that there exists still another form of lead. The element thorium, whose atomic number is 90, is spontaneously radioactive and forms a family of radioactive sequences much as radium does. The end of this sequence is a stable substance that also looks and behaves like ordinary lead.

It was Frederick Soddy who as early as 1910 saw the meaning of these riddles of ionium-thorium and of the three different leads that are alike. With fine courage he predicted that the three leads would have different atomic weights, and that the one from thorium would be greater than ordinary lead while the one from radium would be less than ordinary lead. Independently Kasimir Fajans made a similar prediction. Both turned out to be true. The atomic weight of ordinary lead is 207.2. The atomic weight of thorium lead is 207.9, while the atomic weight of radium lead is 206.1. The one is 0.7 greater and the other 1.1 less than ordinary lead. These values were secured by the great masters of atomic weight determinations, Theodore W. Richards in America, and O. Hönigschmid in Germany, and there was no wishing them away. Here are elements identical chemically but with different atomic weights. How can this be?

Soddy called such substances isotopes, and explained what they represent in terms of atomic structure. In Greek *iso* means alike or the same; and *topos* means spot or space. Isotopes are elements that occupy the same space in the Periodic Table. They have the same atomic number, and the same chemical properties, regardless of what their atomic weights may be.

We have learned that the chemical properties of an element are determined by the number of its electrons outside the nucleus, which of course equals the net number of positive charges on the nucleus. Therefore, if two elements are indistinguishable chemically, they must have the same number of positive charges on the nucleus, the same number of electrons outside the nucleus, and the same arrangement of those electrons in their shells.

However, we have also learned that the nucleus contains more than the protons necessary to give it its net charge. For instance, helium has 2 protons in the nucleus, which give it its 2 positive charges; but because its atomic weight is 4, it has something else in the nucleus that supplies the extra mass of 2.

At this time it had been tentatively supposed that this extra nuclear mass of 2 is furnished by 2 additional protons, each of which is neutralized by 1 electron inside the nucleus. In the same way lithium, with its atomic weight of 7 and atomic number of 3, has 7 protons in the nucleus, of which 4 are neutralized by 4 electrons inside the nucleus, leaving a net nuclear charge of 3.

Now suppose that a lithium atom is composed somewhat differently, as shown in Figure 11. Suppose that it has only 6 protons in the nucleus, and that 3 of these are internally neutralized by 3 electrons. The nucleus still has 3 positive charges, and the atom has 3 outside electrons arranged in 2 shells as before. Since the chemical properties are determined by the electrons in their shells, this atom would be indistinguishable chemically from the regular lithium atom. It would have the same atomic number, 3, and occupy the same spot in the Periodic Table. Its atomic weight, however, would be less by 1 unit than normal lithium; its atomic weight would be 6 instead of 7.

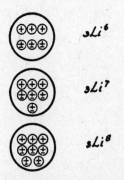

FIGURE 11. ISOTOPES OF LITHIUM

All three isotopes have the same number of protons, and therefore the same net 3 positive charges on the nucleus. Three positive charges also mean 3 electrons. Hence the three isotopes are chemically alike. However, the extra mass of "neutralized protons" makes the difference between the masses of the isotopes, each being 1 unit heavier than its lighter neighbor.

Or suppose that an atom has 8 protons in the nucleus, of which 5 are internally neutralized by 5 electrons. The net charge on the nucleus would again be 3, and the atom would again have 3 outside electrons arranged in two shells. Such an atom would have all the chemical properties of lithium; its atomic number would be 3 and it would be in the same spot as lithium in the Periodic Table. But its atomic weight would be 8 instead of 7.

According to Soddy these three types of lithium would be isotopes: three chemically identical substances with different atomic weights. In this way Soddy explained ionium and thorium, and the three kinds of lead. Ionium and thorium are isotopes; they have the same atomic number, 90, the same number of nuclear charges, the same number of electrons outside the nucleus arranged in the same shells. But they differ in the number of internally neutralized protons present in the nucleus to make up the different atomic weights. Similarly, lead, radium-lead, and thorium-lead are isotopes: they have the same atomic number, 82, with the usual chemical consequences, but they differ in the number of internally neutralized protons in the nucleus that determine their atomic weights.

This idea of Soddy's explains why ionium and thorium, though identical chemically, differ in atomic weight. But how does it explain the fact that neither atomic weight is a whole number? Soddy knew the answer to this. Neither ionium nor thorium is a pure isotope; each is a mixture.

It is simpler to examine lithium. We saw a moment ago that it is conceivable to have three kinds of lithium, which are chemically indistinguishable isotopes: the normal one whose atomic weight is 7, a light one of atomic weight 6, and a heavy one of atomic weight 8. Suppose that ordinary lithium as found in nature is a mixture of two of these three isotopes, the normal one and the light one. If they were mixed in equal proportions the atomic weight of the mixture would be midway between 6 and 7 or 6.5. Actually the atomic weight of lithium is 6.94, which is so near 7 that the light isotope probably occurs about once in 20 atoms of the mixture.

Let us suppose that most elements as they are found in nature are mixtures of isotopes. It then follows that the deviations of atomic weights from whole numbers can serve as a clue to the relative amounts of the different isotopes in the elements as they occur naturally. This has turned out to be true. However, in 1910 it was guess work, brilliant and sublime guess work of the kind that gives one's heart a lift even in retrospect.

Before closing this section we may as well learn how to designate isotopes because we will need them later in the story. Again let us use lithium as an easy example. Lithium has an atomic number of 3. Its common isotope has an atomic weight of 7. This isotope is therefore written as $_3\text{Li}^7$; the subscript 3 indicates the atomic number, while the superscript 7 gives the atomic weight. Its less common isotope is $_3\text{Li}^6$. The theoretical isotope $_3\text{Li}^8$, which I described a while back, has never been found; it is inherently unstable. Frequently the isotopes are just referred to by their weights, and the atomic number is omitted because it is well known. Thus we speak of lithium-6 or lithium-7; and of the nonexistent isotope as lithium-8.

Now we can return to the story itself. Soon after this time many isotopes were discovered, but in a way quite different from what one would expect from the development that drove Soddy to invent them.

2. ISOTOPES IN BUNCHES

Let us go back to our old Geissler tubes and see what happened with them. A Geissler tube is a glass tube from which most of the air has been pumped out and through which an electric current passes between two metal electrodes. One of these plates is negative and from it a steady stream of electrons goes across the space to the other plate, which is positive. The negative plate is the cathode; the positive one is the anode.

As the current passes through the gas in the tube it tends to strip the negative electrons from the atoms of the gas and carry them along, from the cathode to the anode. What remains of the atoms are positively charged ions, which must be moving in the opposite direction, from the anode toward the negative cathode. These streams of positive ions were called positive rays when they were first discovered, and it was their study that developed our knowledge of isotopes.

In order to investigate these positive rays, J. J. Thomson designed a tube somewhat different from those previously used. If positive rays are coming from right to left in the diagram in Figure 12, it would be a good idea to catch them and find out what they are. Therefore, Thomson used a thick cathode, and drilled a long hole in its center, in the hope that the positive rays on their way toward the cathode would go right through the hole and pass beyond it in a straight beam. For this reason he lengthened the tube to the left of the cathode and made arrangements to put a photographic plate at the extreme

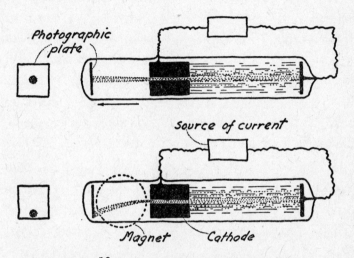

FIGURE 12. DEMONSTRATION OF POSITIVE RAYS

The upper drawing shows the positive rays going through the hole in the cathode and falling on a photographic plate to make a round spot in the center. The lower drawing shows a magnet deflecting the beam so that it hits the photographic plate at a spot lower down on the photograph.

end. He argued that the beam of positive rays would impinge on the photographic plate and make a little black spot the diameter of the beam. And that is precisely what happened.

The next step was even more exciting than the mere demonstration of the existence of positive rays. If these rays are really the atoms of the gas stripped of some electrons, that is, if they are ions, then they should have essentially the mass of the atoms of the gas in the nearly evacuated tube. Thomson knew how to measure such masses, for it was he who had measured the mass of the electron several years before. He used the same principle here. A powerful magnet placed near the tube should divert the positively charged particles from their direct path. Instead of hitting the photographic plate dead center, the beam should hit below or above depending upon the orientation of the magnet. Moreover, the beam of charged particles should be deflected more or less, depending upon the mass of particles. Heavy particles should be deflected less than light particles, and if there are several kinds of ion in the beam of positive rays, there should be several spots on the photographic plate at distances from the center depending on the masses of the ions.

The first gas that Thomson used in this apparatus was neon. Nowadays the red color of neon under such conditions is familiar in the common neon signs. In 1910 it was relatively rare. The gas that J. J. Thomson used was highly purified neon, and when its positive rays were deflected by a magnet and photographed at the other end of the tube, it showed a dense dark spot at a distance from the center corresponding to a mass of 20. Neon has an atomic weight of just over 20 and this fits the requirements.

In addition to this dark spot corresponding to neon,

there was a very much lighter spot farther from the center at a place corresponding to something with an atomic weight of 4. This lighter spot was clearly helium. We already know that helium and neon are both inert gases belonging in the same vertical column in the Periodic Table, and it is easy to understand why one could not remove all the slightest impurities of elements similar to neon. In fact, there was still another spot evident on the photographic plate; this one at a place corresponding to an atomic weight of 40. This also seemed sensible, because argon has an atomic weight of 39.9, and argon is another of the inert noble gases in the same column of the Periodic Table.

So far, so good. However, close examination of the photograph showed a very fine shadow of a spot at a place near neon but corresponding to an atomic weight of 22. J. J. Thomson purified his neon several times; but whenever any tube showed a spot for neon at 20, it always showed a faint shadow at 22. Could it be that there are two kinds of neon, which cannot be separated from each other by chemical purification, a neon of atomic weight 20, and a neon of atomic weight 22? If there were two kinds of neon, then the reason that even the most purified neon gas has an atomic weight of 20.18 is that it is a mixture of the two neon isotopes, with neon-22 present as a small fraction of the mixture.

These observations were made about 1913 in the Cavendish Laboratory, Cambridge University, where

J. J. Thomson was the director. One of the younger men there was F. W. Aston, who thought he saw a way of making certain that these ideas were correct. Aston argued that even if one cannot separate the two neons by chemical means, one should be able to separate them by physical means, using some property that depends on the mass of the nucleus, rather than on the number of electrons. For example, suppose we liquefy neon, and then let it evaporate slowly. The atoms of neon-22 are 10 per cent heavier than the atoms of neon-20. The atoms of the heavier isotopes should therefore find it a little more difficut to hurl themselves from liquid neon into the air and become gaseous neon. The lighter neon will thus evaporate faster than the heavier neon, and after most of the liquid neon has evaporated, the residue should contain a larger fraction of heavy neon than before.

Aston tried out his idea in this way, but failed to find any differences. He therefore tested another method involving the same idea. He allowed neon to diffuse from one container into another through a barrier of baked clay like that used for clay pipes. This clay is a porous material full of microscopic holes, through which the neon atoms would have to travel. Aston argued that the heavy neon isotope should not be able to move so rapidly as the light neon, and therefore that the gas that had passed through the clay barrier would contain less of the heavier isotope, whereas the gas remaining in the original container would have more of the heavier istope. Aston found a just measurable difference between the gases in the two containers, enough to show the probability of the idea, but not enough to settle the matter.

I mention these two methods here because they are typical of the kind that were later used successfully. Indeed, much later they were important in the manufacture of materials for the atomic bomb. Unfortunately their first trials by Aston resulted in little more than encouragement.

This was in 1914, just when the First World War began. Most of the young men in England became occupied with the war, and nothing much happened in the laboratories. Aston survived the war and in 1919, when he again began working in this field, he did not return to the separation experiments, but followed more directly in J. J. Thomson's footsteps.

Aston elaborated the negative end of the Geissler tube to an even greater extent than had J. J. Thomson. In addition to the one hole in the cathode through which positive ions passed, he placed another block of metal with another hole farther to the left as in Figure 13. In this way the stream of positive ions that goes through the first hole, and that has become slightly divergent by the time it reaches the second hole, is sharpened because the second hole permits the passage of only those ions that have gone in a straight line between the first and second holes. By this means a very precise beam of ions is formed, which makes a small spot when it hits the photographic plate at the end of the tube. When a large magnet is put outside near this beam of ions, the beam curves away from its original direction in an arc whose curvature is determined by the mass of the ion. In this way one gets

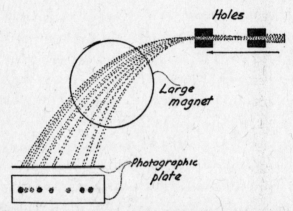

FIGURE 13. MASS SPECTROMETER FOR ISOTOPE SEPARATION

This is the left or cathode end of a Geissler tube, enlarged and modified. The large magnet curves the particles of different mass to different extents, the lighter being deflected more than the heavier.

a series of spots on the photographic plate and the spacing of the spots depends on the masses of the ions which make up the beam. Since the mass of an ion is essentially the mass of its nucleus, this procedure is a method of separating isotopes.

Before the First World War Thomson had found the secondary light spot of neon-22 associated with the darker spot of neon-20, and had recognized them as the two isotopes of neon. With his new and precise instrument Aston found that practically all elements, even when thoroughly purified, have these secondary spots associated with them. It was comparatively easy to determine the relative weights of the ions corresponding to the various spots, and in a short time Aston found the isotopes of many elements. Moreover, since the degree of blackening of a spot depends on the number of ions that hit it, Aston could also gauge the relative abundance of the isotopes of any element. The sketch at the bottom of Figure 13 shows how such a photographic plate looks.

Aston found that almost all the elements that he studied have isotopes. His work was later taken up by K. T. Bainbridge in the United States, and between them, they examined the whole series of elements. All elements have between 1 and 8 isotopes; the 92 elements together have about 250 isotopes. A strange regularity has turned up here. Those elements whose atomic number is even may have up to 8 isotopes, whereas those elements whose atomic number is odd never have more than 3 isotopes. Just why is not clear at present.

Our original question of why the atomic weights of the elements are not whole numbers can now be answered with confidence. Most elements are mixtures of isotopes. The fractions in their atomic weights depend on the relative proportions in which the isotopes exist in nature. If an element has an atomic weight that is very nearly an integer, it is overwhelmingly composed of just one isotope. This is true of fluorine, with its atomic weight of

19.00; of sodium, with its weight of 23.00; and of helium, with its weight of 4.00.

3. A SPECIAL ISOTOPE: HEAVY HYDROGEN

The existence of numerous isotopes presents us with a pretty problem. Very early the atomic weight of oxygen had been assigned the arbitrary value of 16.000. This was fine before one knew about isotopes, and would still be fine if oxygen had no istopes and were just $_8O^{16}$. But oxygen has two naturally occurring isotopes, O^{17} and O^{18}. For every 500 atoms of O^{16} there is either an atom of O^{17} or of O^{18}. If we assign the value of 16.000 to the isotope O^{16}, then the atomic weight as determined with the naturally occurring mixture of oxygen isotopes will have to be higher by nearly 3 parts in 16,000, that is, it will be 16.003.

For most purposes this difference need not even be remembered, because it is so trifling. It does make a difference in the atomic weights of the other elements, which would all have to be raised by the same fraction. Therefore to avoid confusion, the old value of 16.000 for natural oxygen has been retained as the standard. But the difference, slight as it is, did set people thinking about hydrogen.

Without going into the details of the argument one can report that if the hydrogen atom is really just 1 proton and 1 electron, then the atomic weight of ordinary hydrogen is too high by the same amount, that is, by 3 parts in

16,000 or about 1 part in 5000. Please remember that even twenty years ago the atomic weight of hydrogen had been measured repeatedly with the greatest precision, and was known as precisely 1.00778. An error of 0.02 per cent was out of the question. Therefore this difference had to be accounted for.

It could be explained most easily if hydrogen had a heavy isotope. But unfortunately neither Aston nor Bainbridge had been able to find any trace of an isotope of hydrogen. Hydrogen purified and put through the glorified Geissler tube (now called a mass spectrometer) showed only one spot in the proper place, and no more.

There was always the bare possibility that a heavy isotope of hydrogen does exist, but that it is present in so small a concentration as not to affect the photographic plate of Aston's and Bainbridge's mass spectrometer. Computation had shown that if a heavy isotope of hydrogen exists, then its presence as only one part in 5000 parts of normal hydrogen would account for the discrepancy in atomic weight. But how can one demonstrate a suspected isotope in such great dilution that no trace of it can be found by the latest and most refined physical method of measurement?

The possibility, however, was fascinating, and for an excellent reason. The usual hydrogen atom has 1 proton, 1 electron, and an atomic weight of 1. The suspected isotope must have 2 protons in its nucleus, 1 of which is presumably neutralized internally by an electron. This leaves a net charge of 1 on the nucleus, as before, which is balanced by 1 electron outside the nucleus. The weight of this atom is 2, which is twice as much as that of the normal hydrogen atom. This is a real difference in weight.

The difference between neon-20 and neon-22 is only 10 per cent, and Aston's efforts to separate them by diffusion and by evaporation had been largely unsuccessful. Moreover, the efforts to separate chlorine isotopes had also succeeded only very slightly because of the small difference in weight between the two isotopes Cl^{35} and Cl^{37}. However, with hydrogen there was the possibility of an isotope with twice the weight of common hydrogen. If the ideas behind Aston's effort at separating the neon isotopes by diffusion or evaporation are sound, they should work with hydrogen, if they worked at all.

So Harold C. Urey thought, and as a consequence he decided to make the attempt. Urey argued that if liquid hydrogen were allowed to evaporate slowly, the normal light isotope should go off into the air more easily than the suspected isotope that is twice as heavy. Therefore, as the hydrogen evaporates, the liquid residue should become richer in the heavy isotope, until it becomes sufficiently concentrated to show up on the photographic plate of a mass spectrometer.

Urey interested F. G. Brickweddie at the Bureau of Standards, who proceeded to make a gallon of liquid hydrogen. Brickweddie then allowed the liquid to evaporate slowly until all but a gram (1/28 of an ounce) of liquid hydrogen was left, which he shipped to Urey. At Columbia University, Urey and G. M. Murphy introduced a little of this presumably enriched hydrogen into a mass spectrometer, and photographed the positive rays produced, as worked out by Aston. They got the usual spot of hydrogen on the plate, but in addition they found another spot, never seen before, at the place corresponding to an atomic weight of 2. This spot could mean nothing else but the heavy isotope of hydrogen, $_1H^2$.

For this exciting discovery Urey was awarded the Nobel prize in 1934. For some reason this heavy isotope of hydrogen, $_1H^2$, seemed such a unique particle at the time that it was given a special name, "deuterium," and a separate symbol, D. And just as the nucleus of ordinary hydrogen is called a "proton," the nucleus of deuterium was called a "deuteron."

Water is composed of two atoms of hydrogen and one of oxygen. Obviously deuterium can replace hydrogen in all chemical reactions because the two are isotopes. Therefore, it is to be expected that the compound D_2O exists, with two heavy hydrogens in place of ordinary hydrogen. Such a molecule of water is called "heavy water." A small fraction of normally occurring water must be heavy water. It now became a problem of separating these heavy water molecules from ordinary water molecules, or at least of increasing their concentration. Such enriched water was prepared by evaporation of ordinary water according to the same principles that led to the discovery of deuterium in the first place.

The concentration of heavy water in the enriched mixture can be measured by weight. The ordinary water molecule weighs 18, its 1 oxygen atom contributing 16 and its 2 hydrogen atoms 1 each. The heavy water molecule weighs 20 because the 2 deuterium atoms contribute 2 each. This is a difference of 2 parts in 20, or 1 in 10. In the laboratory one can easily weigh with a precision of 1 part in 10,000. Therefore one can detect by weight 1 part of heavy water in 1000 of ordinary water.

The ease and precision of detecting heavy water made it a useful tool in fields other than atomic structure; for example, in physiology. Ordinary water and heavy water are indistinguishable chemically, and even the human body uses them indiscriminately. If you drink some ordinary water today it is not possible to tell how long it stays in the body or where. But if you drink some heavy water, it is possible by its weight to tell the moment it reaches the urine: the water prepared from the urine will be denser than ordinary water.

Heavy hydrogen can be substituted for ordinary hydrogen in a variety of compounds, and their course through the body may be traced in the same way. Indeed, several investigators have studied the path not only of heavy hydrogen but of heavy oxygen O^{18} and of other isotopes as well, so that an entirely new chapter in physiology is now being written.

Deuterium has served as a tool in the further exploration of atomic structure, and heavy water later played a role in the release of atomic energy. The discovery alone of deuterium and heavy water helped to confirm the explanation of isotopes and to strengthen the meaning of atomic weights.

4. THE BASIS FOR ISOTOPES: NEUTRONS

The discovery of isotopes and the explanation of their structure brought into focus a problem that we have lightly passed over. It concerns the mass of the nucleus in excess of the protons furnishing its net positive charge.

It will be recalled, for example, that lithium with an atomic number of 3 and an atomic weight of 7 has 3 protons in the nucleus and 3 electrons outside. Four units of mass left in the nucleus must be accounted for. For a number of years, this extra mass was tentatively regarded as due to 4 protons whose charges have been neutralized by electrons inside the nucleus; and the diagram in Figure 8 on page 69 and in Figure 11 on page 85 are drawn according to this idea.

All the elements above hydrogen have this extra mass in the nucleus; for the heavier atoms it is greater than the mass of the protons responsible for the atomic number and the net charge. Thus uranium has 92 protons with their positive charges, and 146 other units of mass, which were tentatively supposed to be protons whose charges have been neutralized by an electron each within the nucleus.

There were lively arguments as to how an electron can be inside the nucleus and why the positive and negative charges did not annihilate each other. The whole idea seemed strange and no one was satisfied with it. However, the only way to deal with strange things is to ask questions, make experiments, and think about them. Many physicists therefore devoted their attention to the nucleus and tried to explore its structure further by bombarding it with alpha particles from radium, and with protons.

In 1930 W. Bothe and H. Becker sent streams of alpha particles at beryllium, the light metal that is number 4 in the series of elements. What came from the beryllium was a beam of rays with very high penetrating power. Bothe and Becker thought that these rays might be gamma rays like those given off by radium. In this they were later shown to be mistaken.

Frédéric Joliot and his wife Irene Curie, the daughter of Pierre and Marie Curie, made similar experiments in 1932 with beryllium and found that some of the radiation given off by beryllium was able to penetrate a lead shield that normally absorbs gamma rays. In addition, they observed that if a paraffin shield or any other hydrogen-containing compound were placed around the beryllium, the rays that entered the paraffin caused the ejection of protons of very high energy. This phenomenon was difficult to understand, and prompted others to investigate it.

Within the year, James Chadwick repeated these experiments with beryllium, and found, of course, the same powerful rays as had Bothe and Becker and the Curie-Joliots. He determined that the rays could not be deflected by a magnet—a finding that showed them to be neutral and in this respect like gamma rays or x-rays. Chadwick, however, noticed that these rays traveled only at about 1/10 the velocity of light, a speed too slow for gamma rays. Gamma rays travel with the speed of light, since they are a form of light.

Furthermore, Chadwick found that these rays from beryllium, when directed against nitrogen, would give an occasional nitrogen atom a terrific wallop, something that gamma rays could not do, since they will bounce off even such tiny particles as electrons. This impact with the nitrogen atom indicated that the rays must be made of particles, and if they are particles, then they must be neutral particles, because they are not deflected by a magnet.

It was not long before Chadwick was able to show that this neutral particle has a mass of 1, the same as a proton. Very properly he called it a "neutron." For its discovery Chadwick was awarded a Nobel prize in 1935.

The discovery of the neutron resulted in a huge surge of activity in nuclear physics, and is one of the definitive steps on the road to the atomic bomb. For our immediate purposes, however, its discovery resolved the problem of the extra mass in the nucleus. The extra mass is com-

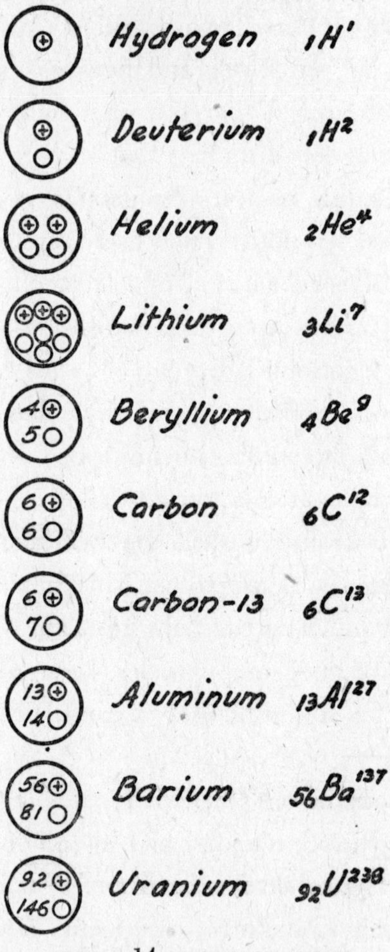

FIGURE 14. NUCLEI OF ATOMS

The number of protons and neutrons in the nuclei are shown for some interesting atoms. For convenience, all nuclei are drawn the same size; actually they differ in size depending on the number of particles in them.

posed of neutrons. The particles inside the nucleus that give it the necessary weight in addition to its protons are the neutrons. The helium nucleus now contains 2 protons and 2 neutrons, and no hypothetical intranuclear electrons are needed. The lithium nucleus contains 3 protons and 4 neutrons, and so on for the other elements.

We may now rest easy. The charge on the nucleus is entirely due to the protons in it. Its mass, and therefore its atomic weight, is determined by the combined mass of its protons and its neutrons. And since the atomic weight of all elements except hydrogen is at least twice its atomic number, there are at least as many neutrons in a nucleus as there are protons.

The nuclei of some of the elements are shown in Figure 14. Notice particularly aluminum with its 13 protons and 14 neutrons; and barium with its 56 protons and 81 neutrons. And above all, look at uranium with its 92 protons and 146 neutrons. All these elements and their isotopes will interest us later.

Meanwhile, here we are with the atom built up as it is understood at present. From now on our task will be to show how it can be split to release the fabulous energy that radium and radioactivity have shown it to contain.

V

ATOMS RELEASE ENERGY

1. MATTER AND ENERGY

At this stage we know three fundamental particles with which all matter seems to be constructed: the electron, the proton, and the neutron. We also know how these particles are arranged inside and outside the nucleus to form that significant sequence of elements represented by the Periodic Table. The picture appears complete, and its pattern seems logically sensible and esthetically satisfying.

True. But it leaves some old questions unanswered, and it raises some new ones. Take the matter of radium. Its atomic number is 88 and its atomic weight 226. We can therefore construct its atom by taking 88 protons and 138 neutrons in a tight bunch and surrounding them with 88 electrons arranged in their proper shells. This structure is designed to satisfy the requirements of the Periodic Table and of a host of chemical and physical properties. But why is this structure so unstable that a small grain of it, all by itself, steadily pours out a powerful stream of alpha particles, beta particles, gamma rays, and heat? Where do the particles and rays come from? Where does the energy come from?

Take the even simpler problem of the neutron. The proton and the neutron both have a mass of 1. Are they related? Is it possible that the neutron is a proton that has captured an electron internally, and has become permanently neutralized? Or, consider the reverse. Perhaps the basic particle is really the neutron, and a proton is merely a neutron that has captured a unit of positive electricity.

This last question requires a moment of explanation, because it has introduced a new concept, a unit of positive electricity. Before 1932 the unit charge of positive electricity had always been associated with the particle of mass 1, the proton. However, there were some possibilities that a positive charge might exist separately from this large mass and that there is a unit of positive electricity with a mass of the same order as the electron but opposite in charge. In fact, P. A. M. Dirac predicted in 1931 that such a positive particle must exist, and in 1932 it was actually found by C. D. Anderson. It is called a "positron." It has a mass as small as the electron and is positively charged. It is not very common, and it lasts only a short time, because it is neutralized almost as soon as it is formed. Can it be that a proton is a neutron that has captured a positron inside itself? No one knows; in fact, the question may be nonsense, but it brings other questions to mind.

What about the positive charges within the nucleus? How do they manage to come so close to one another and remain stable? We know that like charges repel each other, whereas unlike charges attract each other. This principle can be demonstrated by such simple means as bits of paper similarly charged by contact with charged amber. The same is true of magnets: similar poles repel, whereas opposite poles attract each other. Yet in the helium nucleus, for example, there are 2 protons—two positive charges—held close together as a unit. The same problem arises in the nucleus of all elements except hydrogen. There is carbon with 6 positive charges in the nucleus, aluminum with 13 positive charges, and uranium with 92 positive charges. How are these numerous similar charges held so closely together as they must be in the small space of the nucleus?

The neutrons may possibly have something to do with it. Notice that helium, the first nucleus that has more than one positive charge, also has two neutrons in it. One of the striking facts of nuclear structure is indeed that the number of neutrons in the nucleus is at least equal to and usually greater than the number of protons. Do the neutrons serve as the binding medium to keep the protons from flying apart? And if so, where do these binding energies come from? To answer some of these questions we have to examine what at first may appear to be a completely different problem.

Since atoms are made only of protons, neutrons, and

electrons, it is to be expected that the atomic weight of each pure isotope will be a whole number multiple of hydrogen. This is true of a few of the lighter elements such as helium, carbon, and nitrogen to the second decimal place. But as the masses of the isotopes began to be determined more and more accurately, it was found not to be true for most of them, and not even for the lighter ones to the third and fourth decimal places. For example, helium $_2He^4$ turned out to be 4.0028, and carbon $_6C^{12}$, 12.0036.

Remember that this is all on the basis of oxygen as 16.0000. Therefore it might seem that if oxygen were given a slightly different value, everything would come out right. Unfortunately this cannot help, because some of the isotopes actually weigh less than they should, and no amount of arithmetical juggling can make them come out whole numbers. Close study of these circumstances brings out something of first-rate importance.

As usual let us first work it out for a light element like helium. Many accurate measurements have established that, compared with oxygen as 16.00000, the mass of the proton is 1.00758, and the mass of the neutron is 1.00893. Helium is $_2He^4$ and has two protons and two neutrons.

$$
\begin{aligned}
2 \text{ protons} &= 2.01516 \\
2 \text{ neutrons} &= 2.01786 \\
\hline
\text{sum} &= 4.03302 \\
_2He^4 &= 4.00280 \\
\hline
\text{Difference} &= 0.03022
\end{aligned}
$$

As the table shows, the whole of helium $_2$He^4 is less than the sum of its parts. There is no wishing this difference away; it results from the most accurate measurements imaginable. In the formation of helium from its components 0.03022 unit of mass remain to be accounted for.

One cannot say that the mass is lost. Nothing can be lost. Every physical and chemical transaction balances both in mass and energy. What then has happened? The interesting thing is that Einstein had thought about this back in 1905 in connection with the special theory of relativity. At that time, he had suggested that energy and mass are different aspects of the same basic cosmic stuff, and that the two can be converted one into the other. He wrote a simple equation for the relation between the two, which says merely that energy E is equal to mass m.

Energy is measured in units such as ergs or calories or kilowatt-hours, whereas mass is measured in different units such as grams or pounds. To make mass and energy equal, the unit of mass must be translated into the unit of energy. The same holds even when one unit of mass is translated into another. To translate kilograms into pounds we multiply by a constant number 2.2. So 1 kilogram equals 2.2 pounds. To translate inches into centimeters we multiply by a constant whose value is 2.5. Thus 1 inch equals 2.5 centimeters. Einstein showed that the translating constant for converting mass measured in grams into energy measured in ergs is equal to the square of the velocity of light measured in centimeters per second. The velocity of light is usually designated by the letter *c,* and its value is 30,000,000,000 centimeters per second. (This is 186,000 miles per second.) The translation constant is c^2, and Einstein's equation becomes

$$E = mc^2$$

probably the most important equation in history.

In 1905 Einstein wondered how to test this equation experimentally, and suggested that it might apply to the enormous energies released in radioactivity, which had only recently been discovered. Einstein's equation was actually tested with alpha particles from radium by J. D. Cockcroft and E. T. S. Walton. But little did Einstein imagine then that his equation would be demonstrated forty years later on so large a scale as was done at Hiroshima, Nagasaki, and Bikini.

If you compute the energy that the transformation of 0.030 unit of mass yields in terms of the equation, the result is startling. The loss of 0.030 unit of mass in the formation of helium from 2 protons and 2 neutrons represents a disappearance of 3 parts of mass in 400 parts, or about ¾ of 1 per cent. In one gram (1/28 of an ounce) this is a loss of 0.0075 gram. Multiply this by c^2 and you get over 650 million billion ergs of energy. Translated into common units this is about 200,000 kilowatt-hours, which is the current used to run 200,000 lamps of 100 watts each for a 10-hour day. And all this from the slight loss in mass that occurs when ½ a gram each of protons and neutrons unite to form 1 gram of helium.

2. MASS IS CONVERTED TO ENERGY

What happens when ¾ of 1 per cent of matter is transformed into energy and is liberated in the formation of helium from protons and neutrons? The same thing that happens when a rock rolls down the mountainside and settles in the valley: the final situation is more stable than the initial one. The rock high on the mountain is in a relatively unstable position; if it is dislodged, it will roll downhill. When it comes tearing down the slope, it gives out the energy that it had by virtue of its high location. When the rock ends in the valley, it has less energy available than before, and is more stable; it can no longer roll down that hill.

Stated formally, this means that when a system emits energy during a change it is more stable after the emission than before. A ball, when it falls from the top of a house, gives off energy in its fall, and is in a much more stable position on the ground than on the roof. Water in the ocean has poured down from the hilltops and has given off energy that can be used to make electricity. The water in the ocean is certainly in a more stable condition than it would be on top of a hill.

What is true for these physical changes, is also true for

chemical changes. When a chemical reaction is accompanied by the emission of energy, the final compounds are more stable than the initial compounds. For example, the bond between carbon and hydrogen has much more energy than the bond between carbon and oxygen. Gasoline, wood, and TNT have many carbon-hydrogen bonds, and therefore are relatively unstable: they can catch fire or explode. When they do so, they form carbon-oxygen bonds that contain less energy; the energy is given off and the final compounds like carbon dioxide are very stable.

Precisely the same circumstances attend the emission of energy in the formation of a helium nucleus from protons and neutrons: the helium nucleus is more stable than the neutron or the proton. Neutrons quickly become attached to other elements, whereas helium nuclei, which are the same as alpha particles, stand a good deal of knocking around without becoming attached to anything or without being broken into their components.

One way to judge the relative stability of a system is to determine the energy necessary to change it into some other state. Our rock in the valley is more stable than on the mountaintop because a lot of energy is required to drag it up the mountainside to its original position. It takes a lot of energy to break up a helium nucleus into its protons and neutrons. And since it is difficult to concentrate such an amount of energy in order to supply it to the small nucleus, the result is that an alpha particle, or a helium atom, is a very stable particle indeed. However, it is by no means the most stable nucleus. In fact, it is one of the relatively less stable elements, as we shall see.

The loss of mass that occurs in the formation of a nucleus from protons and neutrons is spoken of as its "packing loss." The idea is that the protons and neutrons are packed more tightly in the nucleus than when they are free. The packing loss of an element per unit of atomic mass is secured by dividing its packing loss by the number of units in its nucleus; this we can call its "packing factor." Obviously, the greater the packing factor of an element, the greater is the energy emitted in its formation, and the greater is its stability. It is as if the protons and neutrons were bound more tightly together in the nucleus as a result of the loss in mass and the emission of energy. Because of this idea, the emitted energy is often spoken of as the "binding energy" of the protons and neutrons in the nucleus.

Aston measured the relative masses of the various isotopes in his mass spectrometer, and found that the packing factor of all the elements is not the same. So many regularities have already been discovered in the properties of the elements that it is not surprising to learn that even in their packing factor the elements show a regular behavior. The new regularity that Aston found is simple enough, but it is pregnant with meaning for every inhabitant of the earth. It lies at the very foundation of the process for the release of atomic energy.

Look at the packing factors of the elements shown in Figure 15. Hydrogen has a packing factor of zero, because its nucleus is just a single proton. The value for any other

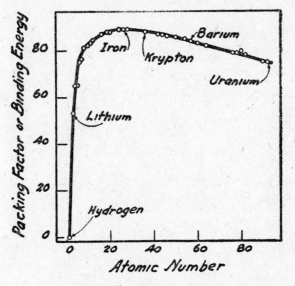

FIGURE 15. PACKING FACTOR

When protons and neutrons form atomic nuclei, they lose some of their mass as a result of the packing or binding of the particles in the nucleus. This loss per particle is the packing factor. It corresponds to the binding energy which is emitted, and its magnitude is shown for some interesting elements. The packing factor is given in hundredths of 1 per cent.

element is secured by subtracting its actual atomic weight from the sum of the weights of the protons and neutrons in its nucleus. This gives the packing loss, which when divided by the number of protons and neutrons in the nucleus gives the packing factor. For example, krypton-78 has 36 protons and 42 neutrons in its nucleus.

$$36 \times 1.0076 = 36.2736$$
$$42 \times 1.0089 = 42.3738$$

$$\text{sum} = 78.6474$$
$$\text{atomic weight of Kr-78} = 77.9262$$

$$\text{packing loss} = 0.7212$$

packing factor
referred to hydrogen $=$ 0.0091, or 91 parts per 10,000

Clearly, krypton-78 has a loss of 91 parts per 10,000 for each of the 78 protons and neutrons that enter into the structure of its nucleus. It must be a stable nucleus indeed.

The drawing in Figure 15 shows the packing factor of many of the elements. They lie on a curve that starts low at hydrogen, rises rapidly to reach a maximum at iron and nickel, and then decreases steadily to uranium. In other words, the light elements and the heavy elements have smaller packing factors than have the middle elements of the Periodic Table. Iron, which is at the top of the curve, has the largest packing factor. It is therefore the most stable element, whereas the lighter and the heavier elements are less stable than it.

Look again at the sequence in Figure 15. Suppose it were possible to convert the elements into one another by rearranging their nuclear protons and neutrons. Then by starting at either end of the Periodic Table and constructing the elements in the middle, we could release energy, since we would be going from less stable to more stable elements. If we started with hydrogen we would combine smaller atoms to make larger ones. If we started with uranium, however, we would break large atoms into smaller ones. In both cases, the final mass would be less than the initial mass, and the difference would be given off as energy. Since we know that a trifling mass becomes tremendous energy either process would yield vast amounts of energy.

Both procedures actually go on; the light-to-heavier transformation occurs in the sun and stars, whereas the heavy-to-light transformation occurs on earth. Hans Bethe of Cornell has shown that the energy coming to us from the sun and stars is emitted during the formation of helium from hydrogen. The process is a rather complicated cycle involving several other elements, but the essential change is the union of 4 hydrogen nuclei to form 1 helium nucleus. In the process, mass is decreased, energy is liberated, and 2 protons are converted into 2 neutrons by the release of 2 positrons. This solution of the old problem of the origin of solar and stellar energy is one of the beautiful accomplishments of modern atomic physics. I wish I could spend some time on it here. But it is only on the periphery of our story and we must leave it with just these few words.

The second way of releasing energy in atomic transformations, from the heaviest elements, occurs on earth. For many years the only known course was through radioactivity. Remember that radium breaks up spontaneously to release helium and radon. The atomic weight of radium is 226, whereas the weights of helium and radon are 4 and 222 respectively. The large unstable nucleus of radium yields the smaller nuclei of helium and radon; mass is decreased because of the larger packing factors, and energy is therefore released. The energy is large, and we computed it earlier in our story.

Several other elements are naturally radioactive, but much less so than radium. The process, however, is the same. Smaller nuclei are formed, and energy is released because of the packing factor relations as shown in Figure 15.

Natural radioactivity is entirely spontaneous. The rate at which radium, uranium, thorium, and actinium normally break up to emit alpha particles, beta particles, and gamma rays is independent of man's activity and nothing we do has any influence on it. However, since 1939 we have learned another method of releasing energy by use of the change in packing factor from heavy-to-lighter elements. It consists in breaking the uranium nucleus up in such a way that the resulting nuclei are substantially lighter than the uranium nucleus and yield up vast amounts of energy. This is the method of the atomic bomb. It can be done at will, and is entirely under the control of man.

8. ATOMS SPLIT AND RELEASE ENERGY: NUCLEAR FISSION

This is a good place to emphasize the fact that in all this work so far physicists were not concerned with the problem of releasing energy to produce atomic bombs. They were concerned with understanding the structure of matter. They wished to explore the nucleus, to determine why protons that are positivey charged and should repel each other, can be in intimate stable contact in so small a space as the nucleus. They wanted to know what a neutron is and how it functions inside the nucleus.

Naturally they could not help speculating on occasions about the release of atomic energy. Some even wrote about the possibilities in the popular press; or at least they talked enough so that the news reporters wrote about the possibilities. However, the experiments that they performed were designed to answer the fundamental questions about matter and energy. The procedure was to bombard matter in bulk with alpha particles, with protons, with deuterons, and after 1932 with neutrons, and to see what happened.

In reviewing this work, one can see now that there were three kinds of result achieved. The first is quite simple, and may be illustrated by the work of Cockcroft and Walton at the Cavendish Laboratory. They found that if a stream of protons at a relatively low velocity is directed against a film of the alkali metal lithium, there emerge alpha particles traveling at a very high velocity.

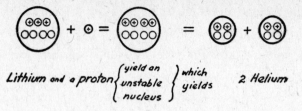

Lithium and a proton { yield an unstable nucleus } which yields 2 Helium

FIGURE 16. LITHIUM FISSION

A lithium nucleus after absorbing a proton splits into 2 helium nuclei with the release of energy.

It can be shown that for each proton that hits a lithium nucleus, two alpha particles appear.

The transformation is simple and straightforward. It is illustrated in Figure 16. A proton is a hydrogen nucleus $_1H^1$. Lithium is $_3Li^7$, its nucleus containing 3 protons and 4 neutrons. An alpha particle is the helium nucleus $_2He^4$ containing 2 protons and 2 neutrons. The process of their interaction may be written as

$$_3Li^7 + _1H^1 = _2He^4 + _2He^4$$

In reading this equation first add the subscripts: 3 protons plus 1 proton equals 4 protons. Then add the superscripts: a mass of 7 plus a mass of 1 equals a mass of 8. Probably what first happens is that the lithium nucleus takes up the proton and for an instant it contains these 4 protons and 4 neutrons, making a mass of 8 with a charge of 4. This nucleus is so unstable that it breaks in two, forming 2 helium nuclei, each of mass 4 and charge 2.

Actually the two helium nuclei fly apart with great speed as if considerable energy were released in the readjustment of the unstable nucleus. That considerable energy is released can be shown in two ways. One is to determine the energy that the proton has before it hits the lithium atom, and the energy of the 2 alpha particles after they have been formed. This is done by measuring the speeds with which the particles travel and computing the energy by the usual equations of standard physics. The difference between the two velocities shows that considerable energy was released in the formation of the 2 alpha particles. After each collision the 2 alpha particles are released with a combined energy of 27.2 millionths of an erg for each atom of lithium.

The other way of showing the release of energy is to consider the loss of mass due to the changed packing factor. The lithium nucleus weighs 7.0165 and the proton weighs 1.0076; together they weigh 8.0241. An alpha particle weighs 4.0028, and 2 weigh 8.0028. Therefore the formation of 2 helium nuclei from lithium and hydrogen has resulted in the loss of 0.0185 unit of mass. This mass is responsible for the energy with which the 2 helium atoms are endowed, and by using Einstein's equation we can compute how much energy this is. The lost 0.0185 unit of mass actually weighs 3.07×10^{-26} gram, which when substituted in Einstein's equation equals 27.6 millionths of an erg per atom of lithium.

Notice how good an agreement the two methods give. In fact, for an experiment of this kind the agreement is almost perfect, and demonstrates the complete equivalence of mass and energy. This, of course, is a proof of Einstein's equation.

One more thing needs to be pointed out about this lithium-proton reaction. It results in the breaking up of the lithium-proton mass into 2 equal fragments—2 helium nuclei. In biology when a cell divides to produce 2 equal daughter cells, the process is called "fission." By analogy the breaking of the nucleus into 2 equal helium nuclei may be called nuclear fission. Actually this term was not used till much later, when in 1939 the uranium nucleus was broken into 2 nearly equal fragments.

The interesting point at the moment is that when a proton and a lithium nucleus collide the result is 2 helium nuclei and considerable energy. Since the whole procedure is man-made, it might seem that this is a method for releasing atomic energy at will. And so it is; but not a very efficient method.

A little reflection shows why. Remember how small a nucleus is compared to the rest of the atom: the diameters are in the ratio of 1 to 10,000. Areas are proportional to the square of their diameters. The ratio of the diameters are as 1 is to 10,000. Therefore the cross-section areas are as 1 to 100,000,000—which means that in passing through a single lithium atom a proton has at best 1 chance in 100,000,000 of hitting the lithium nucleus. The chances are even fewer, because the proton and the lithium nucleus are both positively charged and repel each other. As the proton continues through the atoms, it hits electrons and becomes slowed down until it is finally stopped after having traversed about 100,000 atoms at best. Thus it has about 100,000 chances in 100,000,000 of hitting a lithium nucleus, or 1 chance in 1000. Even if the energy released is high, it hardly equals the energy required to get the protons moving, since at best only 1 in 1000 will hit a lithium nucleus. In short, this is a wasteful and inefficient method. The atomic energy is there, and it can be released; but not for technically useful purposes.

4. RADIOACTIVE ATOMS ARE PRODUCED ARTIFICIALLY

In summarizing the action of atomic projectiles, I said that three kinds of result were achieved. The first is comparatively simple, like the fission of lithium just described. The second is somewhat more complex, and much more revolutionary.

Consider aluminum, the thirteenth element, with an atomic weight of 27. Its nucleus contains 13 protons and 14 neutrons, and it has no known isotope. When aluminum is hit with alpha particles, neutrons are emitted and a substance is formed whose nucleus has 15 positive charges and a mass of 30. This substance should be one whose nucleus contains 15 protons and 15 neutrons. The equation

$$_{13}\text{Al}^{27} + {}_2\text{He}^4 = {}_{15}\text{P}^{30} + {}_0\text{n}^1$$

bears this out; notice that the neutron is written as ${}_0\text{n}^1$ because it has zero charge and a mass of 1.

Now a substance with 15 protons in its nucleus is the 15th element in the Periodic Table, and this corresponds to phosphorous. Note, however, that the atomic weight of this newly formed substance is 30, whereas the atomic weight of phosphorous is 31, and it has no known isotope.

These experiments were made by Frédéric Joliot and his wife, Irène Curie. The Curie-Joliots made chemical tests of this newly formed substance, and found it actually to be phosphorous. Here then was a phosphorous lighter than common phosphorous, which had never been found in nature. It looked as though a new artificial isotope had been produced.

This indeed was exciting; but what was more exciting was that even while the chemical measurements and tests were being made the material seemed to vanish. In a quarter of an hour no phosphorous was left. And most exciting of all, as it disappeared, it was radioactive. It gave off the usual gamma rays, and in addition it gave off the elusive particle that had only recently been discovered, the positron. It will be recalled that this is the positive counterpart of the negative electron which Anderson had found in 1932. It has the trifling mass of the electron but its charge is positive instead of negative. The symbol for an electron is usually written as $_{-1}e^0$, which means 1 negative charge and no mass. The symbol for the positron is therefore $_1e^0$ or one positive charge and no mass.

The final product that appeared after the radioactive

phosphorous disappeared was silicon, a well-known element, which combines with oxygen to make the main constituent of sand. Silicon is $_{14}Si^{30}$. Its formation from radiophosphorous may be conceived in terms of the following equation

$$_{15}P^{30} = {}_{14}Si^{30} + {}_1e^0$$

where $_1e^0$ is the positron ejected in the process.

Where does the positron come from? Look at Figure 17.

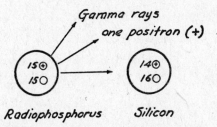

FIGURE 17. ARTIFICIAL RADIOACTIVITY

An unstable phosphorous nucleus spontaneously gives off gamma rays and 1 positron, and becomes converted into silicon. The gamma rays are powerful x-rays, like those given off by natural radium.

Radiophosphorous has a nucleus of 15 protons and 15 neutrons. This is evidently an unstable arrangement in which there are too many protons. As a result, 1 positron is released, which may be conceived of as the positive charge from a proton. If the positive charge of a proton is removed, what remains is a neutral particle, a neutron. The transformation therefore is from a nucleus of 15 protons and 15 neutrons into one of 14 protons and 16 neutrons. This is a common isotope of silicon and was well known from the work of Aston.

The significant aspect of this discovery is not that one element has been transformed into another, because such transmutations had become relatively common by 1933. The revolutionary discovery is that artificially a radio-active element like radiophosphorous has been produced that so far as we know does not exist in nature.

Within a year, most of the easily available elements were tested in this way and practically all of them yielded radioactive isotopes. A whole new group of isotopes was thus artificially produced—isotopes that are radioactive. It is a curious quirk of destiny that artificial radioactivity should have been discovered by the daughter of the Curies, who had discovered the most potent source of natural radioactivity. The Nobel prize in 1935 was awarded to the Curie-Joliots for this work.

The discovery that most elements can be produced in the form of radioactive isotopes opened the most wonderful possibilities—more wonderful than atomic energy in their influence on human life. It will be recalled that one of the virtues of the heavy hydrogen isotope, deuterium, as well as of the heavy oxygen isotope, is that it can be used in biological experimentation to chart the passage of an element through the body. Because it is an isotope of hydrogen, deuterium may be substituted for hydrogen in water, in protein, in fat, and fed to animals. Its heavier mass betrays its presence in the blood, or in muscle, or in the urine, and when these are analyzed, the course of the substance containing the isotope may be followed in the body. This often involves killing the animal to remove the tissue. Moreover, it involves a fairly cumbersome analytical process.

The use of radioactive isotopes facilitates and extends this biological search enormously. In the first place, the radioactive isotope always shows its presence by its radioactivity. No matter where it is, it steadily gives off positrons and gamma rays, which can be detected by the delicate means developed by physicists for their own atomic work. This can be done without killing the animal or destroying its organs.

In the second place the mass difference between light and heavy isotopes limits the work to a few elements only. It is not too easy to separate deuterium from hydrogen even though their masses differ by 100 per cent. It is much more difficult to separate oxygen-18 from oxygen-16, or nitrogen-15 from nitrogen-14 in order to prepare them in the concentrated form necessary for biological experimentation. The heavier elements are even more difficult to prepare, and the whole process becomes too costly for university laboratories to play with.

Artificial radioactivity solves this whole problem at a blow. Almost any element may be prepared as a radioactive isotope, and the preparation of one is about as easy as another. Moreover, the radioactive isotope need not be separated for purposes of concentration; it can be directly produced in the relatively high concentrations that are needed for the preparation of compounds used in feeding or injection.

The third possibility for using radioactive isotopes, though still in the realm of fantasy, is the most fascinating of all. Some organs of the body have a special affinity for one element. For example, the thyroid gland in the neck has a special affinity for iodine, and the bones have a special affinity for phosphorous. We take iodine ordinarily in food and drinking water, and a large part of it goes to the thyroid gland to be stored as part of the material that the thyroid gland secretes. If the iodine were radioactive, a good deal of radioactivity could thus be concentrated in the thyroid gland. All tissues are sensitive to radioactivity because its gamma rays are powerfully destructive to living cells. However, cancer cells are much more sensitive to gamma rays than are ordinary normal cells. Therefore if there were cancer cells in the thyroid, the radioactivity would kill them more easily than it would kill normal cells, and the concentration could be so regulated that the cancer cells would be destroyed locally without injuring the normal thyroid cells. In the same way radioactive phosphorous would settle in the bones so as to destroy a bone cancer.

Let me insist that this is all speculation, that no cancers have been cured this way, and that it still remains to be demonstrated that most organs in the body have affinities for particular elements like the thyroid for iodine. But it is the kind of speculation in which scientists often indulge, and in the testing of which the most unexpected and most useful results may appear. Inherently it is no more improbable than many of the discoveries that have been recorded in the present story of atomic exploration.

Up to now, the radioactive isotopes have been available in pitifully small amounts only. However, we know that in the manufacture of material for atomic bombs many elements can be rendered radioactive in relatively large quantities. These have only just begun to be distributed for experimental purposes, and it is to be hoped that as their use becomes more general in biological and medical research, some of the speculations will become realities.

5. THE NEUTRON BECOMES EFFECTIVE

For our story the most effective particle used in the exploration of the structure of the nucleus is the neutron. The protons, deuterons, and alpha particles, whose actions against various elements I have just described, are all positively charged particles. The proton is the nucleus of ordinary hydrogen, the deuteron is the nucleus of heavy hydrogen, and the alpha particle is the nucleus of helium. Because of their positive charge these particles are repelled by the nuclei of the elements against which they are directed. In order for them to collide with another nucleus and to enter it, they have to travel at great speeds. For years the cry had been for more and more speed, and for more powerful devices to send these particles hurtling at speeds closer and closer to the velocity of light.

Neutrons have the same mass as protons, but have no charge. Therefore they are not repelled by the positive nuclei of atoms against which they are moving, and can more easily come into contact with them. Soon after neutrons had been discovered by Chadwick in 1932, Enrico Fermi in Rome began to use them as missiles to send into the interior of the nucleus. As his work and that of his associates developed in Rome, it was duplicated and amplified by George B. Pegram and John R. Dunning at Columbia University in New York.

The results achieved were not dissimilar from the two types that I have already described. New atoms were formed from other atoms, and radioactive isotopes of various elements were produced. However, the most important result of the work concerned the speed of neutrons. Because the other particles were being used at high speeds, when neutrons were first used they were also jacked up to high speeds. But it soon became obvious that not only was this unnecessary, but even wrong. Slow neutrons were apparently much more effective than fast ones. In fact, neutrons that were so slow as to resemble in speed the ordinary random movements of atoms in a gas were found to be the most effective.

Such slow neutrons easily penetrate the nucleus. Then

if the combination of nucleus plus neutron is stable, the nucleus remains and a new isotope of the element is formed. But if the arrangement of nucleus plus neutron is unstable, it breaks up to liberate positrons or electrons and gamma rays, or it becomes a radioactive element that in its turn liberates positrons or electrons and gamma rays.

The slower the neutrons, the better for these purposes. Neutrons can be slowed down by letting them pass through paraffin or similar substances containing hydrogen or carbon, substances called "moderators," which we shall meet again later. The neutrons are slowed down because they are constantly bouncing against the protons of the hydrogen atoms or against the light and stable nuclei of the other moderators, and the collisions gradually dissipate their energies.

Many things were done with these very slow neutrons. But the one that belongs in our stream of history deals with the relation between neutrons and the heavy elements. Uranium is the last and heaviest natural element in the Periodic Table. Can one artificially produce still heavier elements? Fermi argued that if uranium were surrounded by slowly moving neutrons, some neutrons might enter the uranium nucleus, and possibly stay there. After some slight rearrangement of charges, involving the emission of a positron or an electron or of some small fragment, the result might be a new element, heavier than uranium. These possible elements were referred to as the trans-uranic elements.

The experiments that Fermi made for this purpose were encouraging. Electrons were liberated from uranium, but the results as a whole were not clear. The experiments were duplicated by others, but the results still remained puzzling. In fact, it was five years before these experiments were understood.

Such a delay is not uncommon in the history of science. However, this was 1934 and the state of the world may have contributed to the delay. First Germany, then Austria, and then Italy were being made uninhabitable for many scientists, who were forced to look for refuge in other countries. Forced migration is not conducive to creative thought—peace of mind is a prime requisite. By 1939 America, England, France, and Denmark had become the homes for an international galaxy of atomic physicists.

VI

ATOMIC BOMBS BECOME POSSIBLE

1. THE URANIUM ATOM SPLITS

Early in January 1939 the first clue was discovered that made the uranium-neutron experiments understandable. Otto Hahn and F. Strassmann, two chemists in Germany, had made chemical studies of the products of slow neutron action on uranium. Among the products they were astonished to find barium.

Remember that the uranium nucleus has 92 protons and 146 neutrons. Barium is $_{56}Ba^{138}$, and therefore has only 56 protons and 82 neutrons in its nucleus. Barium is so far from uranium in the Periodic Table that it does not seem sensible for it to appear as a product of neutron action on uranium. All previous experience leads one to expect the emission of a small fragment by uranium, perhaps an electron or a positron, and the appearance of some element immediately near the atomic weight of uranium. But what was barium doing here?

O. R. Frisch and Lise Meitner, in Copenhagen and Stockholm as refugees from Germany, had worked on uranium-neutron reactions; and as Lise Meitner meditated on this curious point, she had a revolutionary idea. Perhaps when uranium absorbs a neutron it splits into two roughly equal fragments. This would account for barium, which has about half the mass of uranium. She told this idea to her friend Frisch. They both discussed it with Niels Bohr, the director of the laboratory in Copenhagen and one of the great physicists, who was just about to leave for a stay at Princeton in order to discuss some theoretical problems with Einstein. Bohr arrived on January 16, 1939, and communicated Meitner's suggestion to his friends in Princeton and Columbia.

The effect of Bohr's news was immediate. I am a biophysicist—one who applies physics to biology—and my laboratory is in the Physics Building at Columbia. Therefore I had some contact with the nuclear physicists who were working there at the time. It was fun to see what Lise Meitner's suggestion resulted in. The weeks immediately following Bohr's arrival were filled with suppressed excitement, with lively speculation, and with critical experimentation. Everybody was working hard, thinking hard, and trying hard to appear nonchalant.

Meitner's suggestion was that when uranium absorbs a neutron it splits into two approximately equal fragments. Why all the excitement?

Uranium has 92 protons. When it splits, barium is formed. Barium has 56 protons, which leaves 36 protons for the other fragment. Look up 36 in the Periodic Table; it is krypton. Now look up barium and krypton in the packing factor diagram in Figure 15. They are among the elements with the highest packing factor. This means that when they are formed from uranium the final mass will be considerably less than the original mass, and a vast amount of energy will be liberated according to Einstein's equation for the conversion of mass into energy.

However, this is essentially no new story, and it should be no cause for excitement. For instance we learned that when lithium absorbs a proton it splits by perfect fission into two helium atoms and releases considerable energy as a result of the mass loss in terms of the packing factor. Moreover, we know that several such energy-releasing transformations have been investigated and that the whole situation is well understood. The energy release is certainly great, but as we have seen, it is useless for technical purposes. Much more energy is required to supply the protons or neutrons necessary to keep it going than can be got out of the reaction. The process stops the moment we stop supplying protons or neutrons.

Precisely here is where the excitement comes in. Look at the diagram in Figure 18. Uranium has 146 neutrons. Barium has 82 and krypton 47; together 129 neutrons. That leaves 17 neutrons to be accounted for. Even if some of these neutrons combine with protons to form small molecules, or become converted to protons, there is the possibility that several neutrons may still be free. It is the possibility of these free neutrons that caused all the excitement.

When one neutron is absorbed by uranium, it breaks in two to give barium and krypton with the release of lots of energy *and with the release of neutrons.* These released neutrons might then be absorbed by other uranium atoms, each of which would split into barium and krypton, and release energy and more neutrons. In this way one might get not only a lot of energy as the result of fission, but several neutrons to keep the process going as a chain

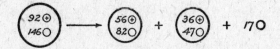

Uranium yields Barium and Krypton and Neutrons

FIGURE 18. NEUTRON RELEASE IN URANIUM FISSION

A uranium nucleus after absorbing a neutron splits into two fragments and releases the extra neutrons. This is the basic fact that makes an atomic bomb possible.

reaction. Such a chain reaction might continue to release energy and to release neutrons, which would be absorbed by more uranium, which would continue the chain until all the uranium would be changed into barium and krypton. The result would be the emission of truly enormous amounts of energy at the expense of just one original neutron, which started the first uranium atom on its path of fission. For the first time the efficient release of atomic energy on a large scale seemed possible.

The first job, however, was to determine whether Meitner's suggestion is true. If the uranium atom that has absorbed a neutron really splits in two, the resulting large fragments will fly apart with great energy. These heavy pulses of energy can easily be detected. Frisch looked for them, and found them almost immediately. Within a few days of one another several groups of investigators here and abroad confirmed the results. Uranium fission is true.

The second job was to see whether neutrons are really emitted during fission. The idea that neutrons might be given off occurred independently to Joliot in Paris, to Fermi, and to Szilard, the last two both at Columbia University. With the help of colleagues they set about determining whether it is true. On March 8, 1939, H. von Halban, F. Joliot, and L. Kowarski sent their report for publication, and on March 16, 1939, H. L. Anderson, E. Fermi, and H. B. Hanstein as well as L. Szilard and W. H. Zinn sent their respective papers in for publication. All three groups of investigators by different methods found that neutrons are emitted during uranium fission. Atomic energy seemed around the corner.

2. WHICH URANIUM ISOTOPE FISSIONS?

The months following the demonstration of uranium fission with the emission of neutrons were full of such activity by many workers in different parts of the world that, in December 1939, when L. A. Turner summarized the year's work in the *Review of Modern Physics*, he covered about 100 papers on fission. Two other elements, thorium and protoactinium, were found to fission. How-ever, whereas uranium works best with slow neutrons, these two need fast neutrons. With all three elements the split is into approximately equal fragments, which turn out to be isotopes of the elements in the middle of the Periodic Table. The elements range in atomic number from 34 (selenium) to 57 (lanthanum); their packing factors are large and therefore much energy is released during the splitting. Most of these fragments are radioactive, and therefore unstable; they emit electrons and gamma rays until they become stable.

In the particular case of uranium fission, the two fragments are only roughly equal: their atomic masses are about 140 and 90. In addition to barium and krypton, several other radioactive isotopes are produced, all of which emit gamma rays.

The most important thing about uranium fission that was discovered in 1939 concerns the uranium isotopes. Uranium has three naturally occurring isotopes. The main bulk of pure uranium—99.3 per cent of it—is $_{92}U^{238}$, which for short is written U-238. A small fraction, 0.7 per cent, is a lighter isotope, of atomic weight 235. It is $_{92}U^{235}$, and is written as U-235. Finally there is a trace of a still lighter isotope, $_{92}U^{234}$, to the extent of 0.006 per cent. Do all three isotopes of uranium undergo fission?

To answer this question it was necessary to separate the three isotopes and to test them individually for fission. We already know that the separation of isotopes is not

easy. Moreover, the differences among the masses of
U-238, U-235, and U-234 are relatively trifling; at best
about 1 per cent. However, not much material is necessary for these tests; so A. O. Nier was able to separate
them by a modification of Thomson's and Aston's method,
which had originally demonstrated the existence of isotopes.

In the mass spectrograph uranium is converted into a
stream of positive ions as in the old Geissler tube. The
stream is passed through holes in the cathode and curved
into an arc by means of a magnetic field. The lighter
isotope curves more than the heavy one, and the two hit
the photographic plate at different spots, as shown in
Figure 13 on page 94. Instead of letting the beams fall
on a photographic plate as Thomson and Aston had done,
Nier permitted them to become deposited on a surface
upon which they could accumulate. Then each spot of
isotope was separately tested with neutrons and the results observed and measured. It was quickly apparent
that only one of the isotopes, namely U-235, underwent
fission. Uranium-238 merely captured a neutron but did
not undergo fission. Uranium-234 hardly enters the picture because of its trifling concentration.

Further investigation showed that U-235 can capture
slow neutrons ever so much more easily than it can
fast neutrons. For purposes of fission, slow neutrons are
therefore best. On the other hand, U-238 captures fast
neutrons more easily, and does not fission.

This information is not good augury for the release of atomic energy. Uranium-235 needs slow neutrons in order to fission. When U-235 fissions it releases fast neutrons. Uranium-238, however, captures fast neutrons and does not fission. To maintain a chain reaction at least one of the neutrons released by U-235 must be captured by a nucleus of U-235. But the liberated fast neutrons are most easily captured by U-238, which does not fission. Moreover, in natural uranium there is 140 times as much U-238 as U-235. The fast neutrons released in the fission of U-235 will therefore be gobbled up by the U-238 nuclei before any of them can be absorbed by a U-235 nucleus to keep the chain reaction going.

There is an obvious way out of this fix: separate the isotopes so that you can have pure U-235 only. Then whatever neutrons are produced in its fission will have a good chance of being captured by U-235 nuclei without competition by U-238, and the chain reaction can have a good chance of going. Alas, this is an obvious way, but not an easy way. We have had experience with isotope separation before, from Aston's first attempts with neon-20 and neon-22 to Urey's successful hydrogen-deuterium separation, and the difficult oxygen-18 and oxygen-16 separation. The 1 per cent difference in mass between U-235 and U-238 did not look propitious for easy isotope separation. Therefore along this road, the release of atomic energy in terms of a chain reaction seemed possible but not likely.

3. NEWLY PRODUCED ATOMS THAT FISSION

The isotope U-238 absorbs fast neutrons but does not fission. What does it do? Nobody was entirely certain, but both evidence and theory seemed to indicate that the usual small fragment emission might be occurring. Indeed in terms of some theoretical ideas that Bohr had formulated, one could guess what might be going on.

It is important to consider these guesses. Admittedly the theory of nuclear structure at that time was poor and limited. Admittedly, prediction in terms of it was more of an art than a science. However, in this particular case, the theory predicted correctly.

What can happen when U-238 absorbs a neutron? If the nucleus absorbs the neutron and retains it, we should get a new isotope of uranium, U-239, because the neutron would merely add to the mass of the nucleus and hence to its atomic weight. Such a first step may be written as

$$_{92}U^{238} + _{0}n^{1} = _{92}U^{239}$$

Add the subscripts for the charges and the superscripts for the masses.

According to theory this is an unstable system with too many neutrons. A rearrangement of charges and masses will therefore take place and the nucleus will emit an electron. If a negative charge leaves the nucleus, it can come about if a neutron has emitted an electron to become a positively charged proton. The result is a nucleus with 1 less neutron but with 1 more proton than U-238.

Uranium has 92 protons; the new nucleus will have a total of 93 protons. An element with 93 protons is a completely different element from uranium, and will occupy the next place in the Periodic Table.

This new element may be called neptunium, with its symbol Np, after the planet Neptune which lies beyond the planet Uranus, after which uranium had been named. It would thus be one of the transuranic elements which Fermi and the others had speculated about beginning in 1934.

The theory also predicted that when neptunium is formed, there will be emitted not only an electron (written as $_{-1}e^0$) but a fair amount of radioactivity in the form of powerful x-rays or gamma rays. The formation of neptunium Np from the transitory isotope U-239 can therefore be written as

$$_{92}U^{239} = {}_{93}Np^{239} + {}_{-1}e^0 + \text{gamma rays.}$$

The process does not stop here. According to the theoretical ideas about nuclear structure Np^{239} should be relatively unstable. In a short while it too will emit from its nucleus an electron and powerful x-rays. The emission of an electron from the nucleus again means the transformation of a neutron into a proton by the removal of a negative charge. From Np, which has 93 protons, we thus derive a nucleus with 94 protons, which constitutes still another new element.

No significant mass has been lost by the successive emission of the two electrons. Therefore the atomic weight is still 239. But the new element is number 94 in the Periodic Table. It was named plutonium, after Pluto the planet farthest out in the solar system. The equation for its production from neptunium is

$$_{93}\text{Np}^{239} = {}_{94}\text{Pu}^{239} + {}_{-1}\text{e}^0 + \text{gamma rays.}$$

The final prediction from theory is perhaps the most significant. It says that the new element plutonium, Pu-239, is stable and that it will absorb slow neutrons preferentially and undergo fission much as U-235 does.

If these theoretical predictions are true, then the absorption of a neutron by U-238 will yield the new element plutonium, Pu-239, which is just as fissionable as U-235 but which can be secured in much larger quantities because of the greater concentration of its parent, U-238, in natural uranium. Moreover, since plutonium is a chemically different element from uranium, there will be no difficulty in separating it from uranium after it is formed, and purifying it.

A mass of plutonium can then be prepared in which to start a chain reaction. A single neutron supplied from an outside source will be absorbed by a plutonium nucleus. It will fission into two flying fragments with the emission of heat, gamma rays, and several neutrons. These neutrons will be absorbed by plutonium nuclei, each of which will fission, emit energy and more neutrons, and this chain process will go on until all the mass of plutonium has been converted into fission fragments and enormous energy.

Thus theory at the end of 1939. And thus fact in 1945.

4. CAN ATOM SPLITTING BE KEPT UP?

All that I have written up to now, and much more, was common knowledge among those all over the world who were capable of understanding it. Much of it is to be found in elementary text books; all of it is available in advanced text books and in professional journals of physics. Far from being secretive, atomic physicists were a gregarious international group, and communicated information and ideas to one another by word of mouth, by mail, by telephone, and even by transatlantic cable. Everybody knew everybody else and everyone knew everything. Ideas were circulated freely, and were discussed critically. As a result enthusiasm ran high and science progressed rapidly.

The year 1939 saw the termination of this free exchange. That summer the Germans had invaded Poland, and Europe was at war. Many scientists reluctantly abandoned their regular work and turned to the problems of war. Some in this country and in England began to think of the military possibilities of a uranium or plutonium chain reaction in the production of atomic energy.

The mere computations were terrifying. The reader who has gone so far in this story can make these computations for himself. He knows the packing factors of uranium and of its fission products barium and krypton. The difference is the mass lost in the fission process, which will be given off as energy in terms of Einstein's equation. The precentage decrease in mass is the same for an atom as for a pound. Therefore he can calculate what would happen with a pound of U-235 pure, if we were to get it free from its isotope U-238. If a chain reaction could become established and all the atoms in the pound of U-235 be fissioned, the energy produced would be over 400 billion billion ergs, or in common units, 12,000,000 kilowatt-hours.

If this energy were released slowly under control it would furnish the electric current that keeps 12 million 100-watt lamps going for a 10-hour day, or about enough to illuminate all the homes in New England for an evening.

If, however, it were released quickly, say in a fraction of a second, it would have the explosive force of about 10,000 tons of TNT. Since there are 2000 pounds in a ton, this is a factor of 20,000,000, and says that pound for pound, U-235 could yield an explosive force 20,000,000 times more powerful than TNT. If only 10 per cent of the atoms in a pound of U-235 were to fission, it would be 2,000,000 times as powerful as TNT; or even if only 1 per cent of the atoms in the pound of U-235 were to fission, it would still be equivalent to 200,000 times the explosive force of TNT. Clearly a new order of explosive force was possible, and the sleep of those who made these calculations was not an easy one.

This is very nice on paper. But in reality no one had established such a chain reaction. No one had separated more than a hundred-millionth of a gram of U-235; this was a microscopic speck on a slide and was used to test which uranium isotope undergoes fission. A pound of U-235, indeed! One had better stay with ordinary uranium with its three isotopes and see what can be done about the possibilities of a chain reaction.

The basic fact is that an atom of U-235 when it absorbs a slow neutron undergoes fission and liberates fast neutrons. In ordinary uranium many things can then happen, and a chain reaction will result only if several factors are just right.

The first is fission capture. Uranium-235 will fission when it captures a slow neutron. Will U-235 fission if it captures a fast neutron? It is quite likely. But we cannot know, because in natural uranium there is 140 times as much U-238 as U-235 and it captures all the fast neutrons without undergoing fission.

Can one slow down the neutrons produced in the fission of U-235 so that they will be captured mainly by other atoms of U-235? One did not know, but there were ideas as to how it could be done. Light elements like hydrogen, helium, carbon, beryllium, and heavy hydrogen do not absorb neutrons easily but bounce them back and therefore slow them down. These are the moderators that

Fermi and Pegram and Dunning had been using all along to produce very slow neutrons. Could one of these moderators be mixed with uranium so as to slow down the fast neutrons emitted by fission and in this way supply the slow neutrons to be captured by U-235 for further fission?

The second factor concerns purity. Most substances capture neutrons and do not fission. Any impurities present in uranium would absorb the emitted neutrons and they would be wasted. Therefore the uranium has to be very pure. Also any moderators for slowing down the neutrons must be pure. The degree of purity is not trivial. Computations showed that impurities cannot be present as more than one part per million. Could one purify uranium or any of the moderators to this extent?

A third factor is the matter of neutron escape. Take a lump of uranium and send in a slow neutron. It hits a U-235 atom, which undergoes fission and releases some neutrons. If the lump is small, these neutrons have a good chance of getting out through the surface of the lump into the air before they are absorbed by some other U-235 atom. Once they get out they are lost, and if more get out than are captured, there will be no chain reaction.

5. THE CRITICAL SIZE OF AN ATOMIC BOMB

There is an amusing and vital point here. In a piece of uranium the loss of neutrons is through the surface, whereas the capture of neutrons is by the mass of the material.

Simple geometry tells us that the volume of a sphere varies as the cube of its radius, while the surface of a sphere varies as the square of the radius. Therefore as a lump of uranium increases in size, its surface does not increase as rapidly as its volume or mass. In other words, the larger the lump is, the less surface it offers per unit mass. Since the loss is through the surface, and capture is by the mass, the larger the lump the greater is the chance of the released neutrons staying inside the mass to be captured by U-235 for fission purposes.

The next question is how large a lump must be so that most of the neutrons get caught, and are not lost through the surface. The critical mass will be that chunk of uranium just large enough so that more neutrons will be retained than are lost. A piece of uranium smaller than this critical mass can never give a chain reaction. A piece larger than the critical mass will do so if all other factors are right.

What is the critical size? This depends on the range of the neutrons in uranium. How far can a neutron go before it is captured? This was known only very roughly, and therefore the critical mass was known only roughly. The available measurements indicated a value between 2 and 200 pounds of U-235 as the critical mass.

Most of the information on the fission of uranium had been secured from specks of the material less than a millionth of a gram in weight. (In case the reader has forgotten—28 grams make 1 ounce.) A critical mass of U-235 weighing between 2 and 200 pounds was just fantastic. No one had ever seen more than a few grams of uranium as a metal all in one place. It was used in making ceramics and steel, but in the most trifling concentrations.

Uranium constitutes between 40 and 90 per cent of the mineral pitchblende, and pitchblende is available in Colorado, in northern Canada, in Czechoslovakia, and in the Belgian Congo. It probably occurs in Siberia. To secure 200 pounds of U-235 would mean first processing tons of pitchblende to get the uranium metal pure, and then separating the isotope U-235 from the 140 times more prevalent U-238 in it. To work with the isotope mixture as it is plus a moderator to slow the neutrons would mean tons of the purified metal.

A similar situation existed with regard to the moderators for slowing the neutrons. Possible moderators were beryllium, heavy water, and carbon; and tons of these would be required just to try out a chain reaction.

Beryllium is a common element, and several hundred pounds of the metal were being produced yearly in the United States. It was not very pure, because there was no need for it.

Heavy water exists normally, as we learned earlier, about one part in 5000 parts of ordinary water. Heavy water can be concentrated by several means, and a large-scale factory for producing a few hundred quarts a year existed in Norway. In the United States a few quarts had been prepared mostly for scientific purposes.

Carbon would be an excellent moderator. It was being produced in relatively large amounts—many hundreds of tons per year—as graphite for lubricating purposes. It was not purified to the necessary extent, but it was at least available and could probably be purified. Its use was suggested very early by Szilard and Fermi.

Suppose one could get enough pure uranium and enough pure moderator to exceed the critical mass and to establish a chain reaction. It might get out of hand. It might blow up. Even if it did not blow up, it might give off enough radioactivity and x-rays to devastate a whole area and make it uninhabitable for months. Therefore one had to look for efficient neutron absorbers—substances that capture neutrons but do not themselves change very much. These could be inserted into the mass so as to control the reaction. A few such absorbing substances were known. One is cadmium, a metal belonging to the ancient triad of cadmium, zinc, and mercury. Others were suspected of being absorbers and would have to be tried out. There seemed to be plenty of work before a chain reaction could be attempted.

VII

ATOMIC BOMBS CAN BE MADE

1. TWO-BILLION-DOLLAR GAMBLE

In January 1939, Meitner had made the suggestion of uranium fission. In a few weeks it had been tested and found true. In a few more weeks most of the computations and ideas just described had been gone through by several people, notably by Szilard and by Fermi at Columbia. The military possibilities had become clear, particularly to a small group of physicists centering around Szilard and including Eugene Wigner, Edward Teller, Victor F. Weisskopf, and Fermi. These were all European scientists who had found refuge in this country from Nazi and Fascist persecution, and they recognized the war clouds in Europe early. Most of our American-born scientists did not think in political and military terms quite so soon as the spring of 1939.

This small group, with the help of Bohr, immediately tried to organize a voluntary stop to the publication of critical data. American and British physicists entered the agreement, but Joliot refused, apparently because of a small paper that had been published before all American physicists had accepted voluntary censorship. Therefore the year 1939 saw the flood of papers on fission that has already been referred to. Actually, voluntary censorship did not begin until April 1940. This voluntary censorship was completely successful and went on for several years, long before any secrecy was established by the military.

It was obvious that to get on with the chain-reaction problem large amounts of materials would be required, more than any university laboratory can afford. Since the military implications were compelling it was logical to turn to the Government for help.

In March 1939 Pegram arranged a conference between Fermi and representatives of the Navy Department. The Navy expressed interest and asked to be kept informed.

Goaded by the possibilities and by the delays, Szilard and Wigner conferred with Einstein in July and decided to appeal to President Roosevelt. This appeal was finally made in the fall by Alexander Sachs, who carried a letter from Einstein with a memorandum by Szilard, and who explained to the President the nature of the problem and the necessity for financially supporting the work. The President appointed a committee of three—one civilian, one Navy ordnance man, and one Army ordnance man—to look into the matter and to advise him.

This committee met several times and listened to evidence; and it made recommendations. Finally on February 20, 1940 the first funds from the Army and Navy

were transferred to Columbia for the purchase of critically
necessary materials. Total transferred—$6000.

The committee met again on April 28, 1940 and listened to reports of progress. By this time research had
demonstrated that of the three uranium isotopes only
U-235 would fission, and that slow neutrons are more
effective than fast ones. Also the measurements on graphite at Columbia had shown that it would be a good
moderator. Above all, news had reached various scientists that a large section of the Kaiser Wilhelm Institute—
the greatest research institute in Germany—had been set
aside for work on uranium. A special advisory group that
met in June 1940 reported to the committee that $100,000
worth of uranium and graphite was required to try out
a chain reaction, and that $40,000 would be necessary to
make the fundamental measurements.

Before it could act on these recommendations the committee ceased to function. In June 1940 the whole problem of civilian scientific aid to the military had been given
to a newly organized group, the National Defense Research Committee (NDRC), and a reconstituted Uranium
Committee had been set up in its framework. It was composed almost entirely of civilian scientists. It had some
funds, and it arranged contracts between NDRC and
various research institutions.

The first contract was signed November 8, 1940 and
assigned to Columbia University. It ran from November 1,

1940 to November 1, 1941, and was for $40,000. Other contracts were soon granted. During the year one went to Columbia for Urey to separate uranium isotopes by the centrifuge method, which I shall describe in a moment. Other contracts went to Princeton, Cornell, Chicago and other universities and research institutions. By November 1941 sixteen such projects were under way. Total appropriation: $300,000.

There is little point to recounting the detailed administrative history of what happened subsequently. However, it is desirable to give a general picture of the events. For a long time the military was not impressed; it was willing to go along, and it supplied some funds. The problem was in the hands of civilian scientists. These were of two kinds. One was a small group of enthusiastic and imaginative insiders who were frantic and frustrated by delays. The other was a larger but much less excited group who wanted to go from one established point to the next and to whom the amounts of money involved seemed large and the chances very small. Actually, in the early days of NDRC the amounts of money allocated to other researches were larger than for the uranium work; but the other researches seemed immediate in application, whereas the atom bomb seemed remote indeed.

The British had of course been thinking along lines similar to ours. Chadwick was certain that a bomb of U-235 could be made. As a whole the British group wanted to concentrate on the separation of U-235 from

U-238 by diffusion on the principle that I have already described for neon-20 and neon-22 separation. Moreover, Cockcroft had suggested the possibility of plutonium though the British never pursued it, probably because of their limited manpower. The British naturally had thought of moderators for slowing the neutrons emitted by the fission of U-235, in order to attempt a chain reaction with ordinary uranium. They had even decided on heavy water as the moderator and had begun to collect it for this purpose.

During 1940 and 1941 there had been both formal and informal exchanges of information between the British and our own scientists. In general the British scientists were more optimistic about atomic bomb production than our official NDRC advisors, and they supported our small but active group of enthusiasts.

One of the critical events of the early days was the journey to England in the fall of 1941 by Urey and Pegram to see at first hand what the British uranium situation was. Pegram and Urey brought back much information, but most important, they carried back a sense of urgency which even in the cold report communicated itself to the administrative group here.

The gist of all this information was conveyed to President Roosevelt and Vice President Wallace. As a result the decision was made in December 1941, just before Pearl Harbor, to broaden the uranium program, to provide funds from a special source, and to work closely with the British. Thus ended the year 1941 with us in the war, and with some real prospects for the uranium work.

The changed psychological situation was important. Even in 1940 Szilard, Fermi, and Wigner did not need to be convinced of the possibility of an atomic bomb. But many other people had been either lukewarm or frankly skeptical. By the end of 1941, the idea had been sufficiently talked about so that a number of administratively powerful scientists had become familiar with it and with its meaning for the war. They decided that the uranium project had to be pushed vigorously.

2. CAN URANIUM FISSION MAINTAIN ITSELF?

During 1940 and 1941 material was being purified and accumulated to test the possibilities of a chain reaction. This work was under the general leadership of Pegram at Columbia with Fermi and Szilard in actual charge. In the early months of 1941 extremely pure carbon in the form of graphite had been prepared sufficient to make a column 3 x 3 x 8 feet. By placing a neutron source at the bottom of this pile, and measuring instruments in various positions inside, one was able to study the properties of the neutrons as they traveled through carbon.

As a result a most important new idea was developed, which in practice became called a "lattice pile."

A lattice pile is essentially a pile of graphite bricks arranged with small spaces between them. At regular locations equally distributed throughout the pile are placed small pieces of ordinary uranium metal. This sharp separation of graphite as moderator from uranium as neutron producer has a special virtue. The fast neutrons emitted by the fission of U-235 leave the small uranium lumps easily, but before they reach the next lump of uranium in the pile, they must go through a given thick-

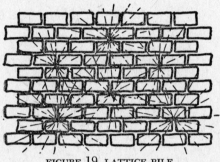

FIGURE 19. LATTICE PILE

Bricks of graphite separate small lumps of ordinary uranium. In this way fast neutrons released by U-235 in any one lump must pass through a lot of moderating graphite (carbon) before reaching another lump of uranium. This passage through the carbon slows down the neutrons, so that they may be captured by U-235 in another lump.

ness of graphite carbon and therefore are slowed down so that they will be absorbed by the U-235 atoms and cause them to fission. The drawing in Figure 19 illustrates the idea.

By July 1941 the graphite-uranium lattice had reached a cube 8 x 8 x 8 feet in size and contained 7 tons of purified uranium. This pile was located in the basement of Schermerhorn Hall at Columbia. At the bottom of the cube was a radium-beryllium mixture, which served as a source of neutrons.

The object of the pile was to determine what became known as the multiplication factor. It will be recalled that several circumstances have to be just right in order for a chain reaction to occur. Suppose these factors balanced so well that for every atom of U-235 that fissions, one of the emitted neutrons will finally be absorbed by another atom of U-235 and cause it to fission. If this goes on, each atom that fissions produces another atom that fissions and so on.

Let us start with 100 U-235 atoms, each of which has received a neutron from the outside source. If as a result of the correct balance of factors the fission of these 100 atoms ultimately results in 100 other U-235 atoms getting a slow neutron each so that they can fission and produce a neutron each, and so on, then the multiplication factor is 1.00 and the chain reaction will just maintain itself. If the factors are such that from the neutrons emitted by the original 100 atoms, 105 neutrons manage to survive and get to U-235 atoms, then 105 atoms will fission. The multiplication factor is now 1.05 and the reaction will slowly increase in speed. However, if from the neutrons emitted by the original 100 atoms of U-235 only 95 manage to be captured by other U-235 atoms, the reaction cannot maintain itself. Its multiplication factor will be 0.95 and the reaction will stop soon.

In September 1941 the pile was large enough to test,

and Fermi reported the multiplication factor to be 0.87. In other words, under the conditions of the pile the chain reaction could not be sustained. However, even though the value was less than 1.00, it was not too far from 1.00 and Fermi felt that it could be increased by improving the purity of the components, the size of the pile, and the arrangement of the substances in the lattice. But could the multiplication factor ever become greater than 1.00? No one knew for certain, and this remained the basic question. In fact it was not answered until more than a year later.

3. NEWLY CREATED ATOMS FOR BOMBS

While this was going on at Columbia other groups in other universities were investigating different possibilities. The most important of these was at the University of California under the general leadership of E. O. Lawrence and the immediate direction of E. Segré. This group concentrated on the problem of what happens to U-238 when it captures fast neutrons. We know what the theory is; but is it really true that after U-238 absorbs a neutron it gives off an electron and becomes $_{93}Np^{239}$, the new element neptunium? And does this new element give off still another electron from its nucleus to become $_{94}Pu^{239}$, the new element plutonium? And is plutonium just as fissionable as U-235?

The importance of the reactions is apparent when we recall two points. One is that U-238 constituted 99.3 per cent of ordinary purified uranium. If U-238 can be converted into fissionable material resembling U-235, then its mere availability of 140 times as much as U-235 is a great asset. The other point is that plutonium is a different chemical species from uranium. After formation it can be separated from the unchanged uranium by relatively simple chemical procedures.

Before the end of the year 1941 the California group had established that U-238 by the capture of one neutron does go through neptunium to form plutonium, and that plutonium is actually fissionable with slow neutrons just like U-235. This had been accomplished with about one millionth of a gram of uranium.

The actual demonstration of the formation of plutonium and of its fissionable character presented the steering uranium committee with alternative paths to follow. One was to separate the isotope U-235 from U-238 and prepare it in sufficient quantities for a bomb. The other was to make plutonium from U-238, and to prepare *it* in sufficient quantities for a bomb.

Under normal conditions one would evaluate the relative chances of reaching the goal by the two paths, choose one, and concentrate all efforts on it. These, however, were not normal times, and both paths had to be explored and developed.

Similar situations arose all through the next four years. Whenever two or more possibilities existed, all of them had to be developed.

This should be remembered when we ask how much the bomb cost. It should also be remembered when we ask how long it would take other countries to produce similar bombs. If our scientists could think of two or three ways of doing something, other scientists would very likely think of at least one way. Perhaps, knowing that a bomb can be produced, they might even think of a different and possibly a simpler way.

4. THREE OTHER WAYS TO GET BOMB MATERIAL

Our story has now ceased to be a single development that like a continuously numbered route on a road map can be followed across the country. Instead it has become a land actively traversed in many directions by several groups of explorers. All of it is in work simultaneously. To follow it we travel for short stretches on one route, then another, and then a third, and only occasionally do we get an air-view of the whole activity.

Let us consider the separation of U-235 from U-238. These are isotopes and cannot be separated by means that depend on chemical differences. Only by their slight difference in weight of 3 parts in 235 can they be isolated from each other. This path of physical separation branches into 3 forks.

The first is magnetic, and is by means of the mass spectroscope. Remember Thomson's first separation of neon-20 and neon-22 at the cathode end of a Geissler tube. Remember also Aston's much enlarged and ampli-

fied apparatus with which he first showed the existence
of isotopes in bunches. The idea is to ionize an element
and make a stream of ions that then passes near a powerful magnet. Because of any difference in charge or mass
the elements in the stream will be spread out and deflected to different extents, and may be caught in differ-

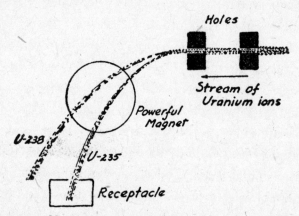

FIGURE 20. MAGNETIC SEPARATION OF URANIUM ISOTOPES

*The powerful magnet deflects the lighter isotope more than it does
the heavier, and enables the lighter isotope U-235 to be accumulated in the pure state free of U-238. Compare Figure 13.*

ent places. Normally, they merely collect in different
spots of a photographic plate to record their presence
for the investigator to measure.

All this can be done for uranium. It can be vaporized
and ionized in a partial vacuum. As a positive ion stream
coming through the holes in the cathode it can then be
spread by a powerful magnet into two streams, one of
U-235 and the other of U-238, as shown in Figure 20.

Then instead of falling on a photographic plate the U-235 beam passes through a hole and is deposited in a receptacle beyond the hole, while U-238 remains behind and is deposited separately.

The California group worked on this and by December 1941 they reported that a millionth of a gram of U-235 reasonably free from U-238 could be separated per hour. At the rate of one millionth of a gram of U-235 per hour, it would take 450,000,000 hours to deposit 1 pound. This is roughly 60,000 years. One could hardly wait for this procedure to furnish material.

Could the separation be done on a large scale? It probably could. However, special machinery would have to be designed and built. Pilot plants would have to be constructed and tested, and a new industry would have to be established. It would take much money and many men. We were at war, and both materials and scientific men were at a premium.

A second method of physically separating U-235 and U-238 depends on the centrifuge. A centrifuge is a fancy name for a cream separator. When milk is whirled around and around in a cream separator the lighter part, which is the cream, rises to the top, whereas the heavier part, the milk, sinks to the bottom. Could one whirl uranium in a gaseous or liquid form around and around so that the difference of 3 parts in 238 by weight would bring the lighter U-235 to the top and leave the U-238 on the bottom?

Toward the end of 1941, the most careful experiments under the general direction of Urey at Columbia showed that it could be done. Calculations from the theoretical developments of this idea by Karl Cohen give some notion of the magnitude of the process. To get 2 pounds of U-235 a day would need the full operation of 22,000 extremely high-speed centrifuges, each about 3 feet long. In addition to centrifuges, there would be needed factories for converting uranium into compounds that are liquids or gases. Pumping units, refrigeration plants and all the machinery of heavy industry would be required. It could be done; but it would take time, men, and millions of dollars.

A third method that relies on the difference in weight between U-235 and U-238 is that of gaseous diffusion. This was the method tried by Aston for neon-20 and neon-22, and had been encouragingly successful. It had been used later for separating the isotopes of the green gas chlorine.

The first step is to convert uranium to a compound normally a gas. This step is simple because a compound of uranium and fluorine is such a gas. The gas is uranium hexafluoride and was called by this name. It may interest the reader to know that for the sake of secrecy uranium was called Tube-Alloys by the British. The gas was therefore referred to by them as Tube-Alloys hexafluoride. If this gas is pumped through tiny holes in a plate, the gas molecules containing the lighter isotope U-235 will go through a little faster than the ones made with the heavier U-238 isotope. Once the gas has gone through the barrier, it will be slightly richer in U-235 than in U-238. To make it still richer, it can be passed through another barrier, and then through another barrier, and so on until a gas very rich in U-235 is obtained.

Experiments and computations at Columbia showed that to get 2 pounds of uranium-235 per day would need about 5000 stages of diffusion one after the other. The barrier plates through which the gases would be pumped would have an area equal to several acres. A first estimate of the cost of such a plant was over 20 million dollars.

Still a fourth method was tested at the Bureau of Standards in Washington. It was a variant of the diffusion method, and work on it was continued at the Naval Research Laboratory. It looked quite promising. To my knowledge it was later abandoned. I merely mention it to show the variety of ideas available.

5. MONEY BEGINS TO FLOW

We are now at the end of 1941. Fermi had found a multiplication factor of 0.87 with the lattice pile at Columbia. At California plutonium had been demonstrated chemically and its fissile properties confirmed. The California group had even suggested that if a chain reaction were established in the U-235 of a lattice pile made up of ordinary uranium and graphite, the excess neutrons could be used to convert U-238 to plutonium-239. In this way the pile would manufacture plutonium under its own power. At least three methods of separating U-235 had been worked out. They had been tested on a small scale and estimates had been made of the cost of setting them up in large-scale production.

It was at this moment that Urey and Pegram came back from England and brought with them the sense of urgency that prevailed there. The Germans had overrun Denmark and had conquered Norway. Holland and Belgium had fallen and France had been defeated. It was after Dunkerque.

In Norway the Germans had immediately taken possession of the only large factory in the world for the production of heavy water. What did they want with heavy water except to use it as a moderator for slowing down neutrons in a uranium chain reaction? It will be recalled that we had considered heavy water for this purpose, but had turned to graphite as a moderator. However, heavy water was being produced by Urey in case it proved necessary. The British had decided to use heavy water, and so had the French. In fact, Joliot's last act before leaving Paris had been to send to England the several quarts of heavy water that had been slowly accumulated in France.

By this time too the scientific effort of the war had become enormous. The original National Defense Research Committee (NDRC) had become the much larger Office of Scientific Research and Development (OSRD)

headed by Vannevar Bush and composed of two divisions
with many sections each. These were civilian organiza-
tions run by scientists, who studied the problems and
allocated funds in the form of contracts to universities
and research institutions for their investigation.

In November 1941 the Uranium Section of NDRC had
become Section S-1 of OSRD, and in December 1941 an
all-out effort was decided upon. The section was organized into a planning board of scientists, and a group
of three scientific program chiefs. In addition Bush
appointed a separate planning board that would be
responsible for the technical and engineering aspects of
the work, for procurement of materials, and for construction of pilot plants and full-size production plants.

Naturally, political policy was not the province of
scientists and engineers. The Top Policy Group concerned
with such decisions was the President (F. D. Roosevelt),
the Vice-President (H. A. Wallace), and the Secretary
of War (H. L. Stimson), the Chief of Staff (G. C. Marshall), the Director of OSRD (V. Bush), and the Director
of NDRC (J. B. Conant). At a meeting of the Top Policy
Group in December 1941, at which Wallace, Stimson,
Bush and Budget Director H. L. Smith were present, it
was decided "that OSRD should press as fast as possible
on the fundamental physics and on the engineering planning, and particularly on the construction of pilot plants."
Bush estimated the cost of this phase of the work as about
5 million dollars. Bush also suggested that the Army take

over when full-scale construction began, and requested that a competent Army officer be assigned early to learn about the problem.

Things really began to happen then. The three program chiefs were E. O. Lawrence of California, A. H. Compton of Chicago, and H. C. Urey of Columbia, who vigorously pursued programs that I shall consider in a moment. With relatively minor administrative changes the scientific and engineering development work continued under OSRD until the spring of 1943, when it was taken over by the Manhattan District.

In August 1942 the problem had reached the point where large-scale production was clearly called for. Following Bush's advice production was taken on by a new organization formed by the Corps of Engineers of the Army. It was labeled DSM (Development of Substitute Materials) and was known as the Manhattan District. It was first set up by Colonel J. C. Marshall, and in September 1942 Major General L. R. Groves was placed in charge. This organization later took over the scientific research and development as well. In January 1947 it was superseded by the civilian Atomic Energy Committee.

6. URANIUM FISSION MAINTAINS ITSELF

Regardless of all the superorganization and regardless of all the urgency, by January 1942 no chain reaction had yet been established. This situation was merely because it required time and apparatus to purify the requisite amounts of materials and to study the best way of making a pile. Whatever was done on the rest of the program had to be done in the faith that a chain reaction would proceed when the critical mass of material was accumulated and properly arranged.

One of the first acts of Compton after the reorganization was to move much of the Columbia group to Chicago. This included Fermi, Szilard, Anderson, and Zinn. The new place in Chicago was called the Metallurgical Laboratory and its spreading growth occupied all the neighboring buildings and beyond.

The job of highest priority for the group was the chain reaction. All during 1942 graphite and uranium were procured and purified. Experimental lattice piles were constructed to learn the properties of the materials and the piles. By the fall enough materials were available to have another try at a lattice pile that would yield a self-sustaining chain reaction.

The pile was constructed under the squash courts in the Stadium of the University of Chicago. As before, bricks of graphite were set up between which lumps of uranium were placed at regular distances. One precaution was taken. Removable rods of cadmium were inserted in various parts of the pile. Cadmium absorbs neutrons and is not changed by them. A rod or plate of cadmium serves as a shield to retard neutron transmission from point to point, and thus serves to control the speed of the reaction. And a good thing it was to have these retarding rods, because the pile worked better than its producers expected. By December 1, 1942 everything at the squash courts was ready to go.

By a curiously dramatic coincidence this was precisely the time when a reviewing committee arrived at Chicago to evaluate the progress of the Metallurgical Laboratory. The most decisive moment in the scientific history of the whole development occurred on December 2, 1942 when the pile was started. It maintained itself. For the first time in the history of the world, human beings had initiated a self-sustaining nuclear chain reaction.

VIII

ATOMIC BOMBS ARE MADE

1. SMALL-SCALE PRODUCTION OF THE NEW ATOM PLUTONIUM

The construction of a self-sustaining chain-reacting lattice pile solved two problems at once. First, it showed that a U-235 chain reaction is possible; therefore atomic energy from the packing loss in the nucleus is available for technical purposes if released slowly, or for a bomb if released rapidly. Second, it showed that plutonium, which behaves like U-235, can be manufactured in the pile.

When a lattice pile is self-sustaining it means that each fission of a U-235 atom produces neutrons of which at least one reaches another U-235 atom that fissions and continues the chain. But as we learned before, the fission of a U-235 atom produces more than one neutron. What happens to the other neutrons? These are captured by U-238, which is converted into neptunium and finally into plutonium with the emission of radioactivity. In other words a pile is an atomic factory to convert U-238 into Pu-239. The medieval philosopher's stone had finally been realized on a mass-production basis.

From now on, plutonium production became essentially an engineering problem. The Manhattan District had already been formed and it took over at this point. It then induced E. I. du Pont de Nemours and Company to undertake large-scale manufacture. The du Pont Company accepted the undertaking but stipulated that the work was to be done without profit and without any patent rights going to it. Since du Pont was entering a totally new field—physics rather than chemistry—it was agreed that the Metallurgical Laboratory at Chicago would still do most of the fundamental research and development, while du Pont would contribute its engineering and industrial experience.

Even while the work on experimental piles had been going on, members of the Metallurgical Laboratory had discussed methods for building large industrial plants to produce the amounts of plutonium required for bombs. Preliminary designs had been drawn well before the first self-sustaining pile had been successfully put together. This pile was being run at almost its minimum capacity so that the emitted heat and radioactivity would be small. Under these conditions it would take about 300 years to produce 1 pound of plutonium. Obviously the industrial units would have to step up the rate of production.

It is worth a moment to explain what is involved. Suppose that from a source outside the pile a single slow neutron is supplied to 1 U-235 atom. It will fission, and produce neutrons. If only 1 of these emitted neutrons reaches a U-235 atom that fissions and emits neutrons of which only 1 reaches another U-235 atom and so on, a chain reaction will proceed. The multiplication factor will be 1.00. At any moment there will be just 1 U-235 atom undergoing fission and the chain will be maintained through this succession of single atoms.

Suppose, however, that we start the series with 100 slow neutrons each causing a U-235 atom to fission. Then the reaction will also just maintain itself, but through 100 chains. The multiplication factor will still be 1.00, but instead of 7 maids with 7 mops, we shall have 700 maids with 700 mops. More plutonium will be produced, more heat liberated, more radioactivity generated. If this is so, then why not 1000 initial atoms, or 1,000,000,000 initial atoms? There is no limit except the heat and radioactivity.

To take care of heat and radioactivity the plants have to be built far from people and from centers of civilization. However, they must be near an extensive power supply so that the plants can have the necessary electricity and the workers in the plants can have homes in which to live. Also the plants should be near a large supply of cold running water for cooling the piles.

The first plant was built at Oak Ridge, in the Tennessee Valley, as the Clinton Engineer Works. The site is remote, but it is near the great power supplies from the TVA. The designs and plans were well along in January 1943, and construction began soon after. Later additions were made, but from the beginning it contained research laboratories as well as production plants. It is a staggering project, as the many photographs show, yet it is much smaller than the final plants at Hanford. The purpose of the Clinton plant was to produce some plutonium and to serve as pilot plant for the chemical separation of plutonium from uranium.

Plutonium is formed from the U-238 in the pile. Means had to be found for chemically removing the plutonium from the other materials. This demanded a knowledge of the chemistry of plutonium, and was also one of the tasks of the Metallurgical Laboratory. In itself this is a fascinating story, because plutonium in microscopic quantities had to be made in one place (at California, and later at Washington University in St. Louis) and its properties and reactions studied elsewhere. At the end of 1942 about 500 millionths of a gram of plutonium compounds had been produced in pure form. This seems like an absurd amount, but for the microchemists it was ample because they can make experiments with just 1 millionth of a gram.

The scientific information gained in these ways had then to be translated into large-scale production methods, and this was the job of the chemists and engineers at the Clinton separation plant. They accomplished this beautifully so that their procedures served as the basis for the Hanford Plant. In addition, the Clinton laboratories served as a training center for persons later to take over the Hanford plant, for medical studies, for testing, and for innumerable side problems that arose.

2. LARGE-SCALE PRODUCTION OF PLUTONIUM

The final large plutonium plant was built as the Hanford Engineer Works on the west side of the Columbia River in central Washington north of the town of Pasco. Near by was the Coulee Dam, which could supply it with power, and next to it was the Columbia River, part of which could be diverted to run through the piles for cooling purposes.

The construction of the Hanford works is one of the triumphs of modern engineering. Ground was broken on April 6, 1943 for the construction camp. At the height of activity in 1944 there were 60,000 inhabitants of the camp, making it the fourth city of the state. The construction of the first pile was begun on June 7, 1943, and it started to function four months later.

The design of these piles for the large-scale production of plutonium is somewhat different from the design of the one built in Chicago. It is shown in Figure 21. The graphite is now in a practically continuous mass with imbedded pipes through which cool water circulates. The uranium is not in small lumps but in the form of slugs or rods that can be slid in and out of tubular holes.

The uranium rods are sealed in cans for easy handling. This itself was one of the minor headaches at Chicago.

For months the precise material to hold the slugs of uranium was under experimental investigation. It had to be something that would not corrode, would not be affected by radiation, would conduct heat easily, and would be available in large quantities. Aluminum turned out to be the best material.

The cooling water was another problem. Obviously the

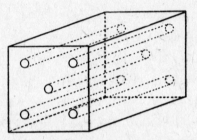

FIGURE 21. THE CONTINUOUS PILE FOR MAKING PLUTONIUM
The graphite is not in bricks, but is packed solid, while the uranium is in the form of rods that are pushed into the tubular holes. The changed U-238 can then be removed and processed for plutonium. Compare the lattice pile in Figure 19.

water could not be heated too high because of the animals and plants with which it would come in contact when it returned to the river. Moreover, the water absorbed some of the radioactivity and therefore had to be stored until it became safe again for return to the river.

After some of the uranium in the pile has been converted to plutonium, the rods have to be transferred to a separation plant for the chemical removal of plutonium. One cannot wait until all the uranium has been converted into plutonium because of the heavy formation of other products of fission that are accumulating. The fission products are intensely radioactive and the material naturally cannot be handled in ordinary chemical ways. Thick walls of concrete have to be built between the workers and the chemical vats, and the processes of removing, dissolving, precipitating, and washing is done by automatic machinery manipulated by remote control.

In this small volume there is no place to describe details. Many of these details raised problems that engineers face and solve every day whenever they are presented with tasks requiring ingenuity, skill, and technical imagination. Some arose out of the special circumstances of radioactivity, of speed, of lack of pilot-plant experience and the like. The total result was one of the extraordinary enterprises of our time. It is to be hoped that the whole story of the Hanford and Clinton plants will some day be revealed in the detail that it deserves.

3. URANIUM FOR BOMBS IS PRODUCED IN QUANTITY

We have followed the path of plutonium production. In 1943 this seemed the most likely to succeed rapidly. However, the other path, the one through uranium isotope separation was not neglected. Several different projects were concerned with the segregation of U-235 from its much more prevalent companion U-238. One of the successful large-scale methods was the gaseous diffusion process.

The principle of the diffusion process is years old. In 1896 Lord Rayleigh had shown that a mixture of two gases of different atomic weight can be partially separated by letting it diffuse through a porous barrier. Aston in 1913 had tried this method for separating neon-20 from neon-22.

In the fall of 1940 John Dunning at Columbia reviewed the prospects of the method and initiated preliminary experiments with funds supplied from one of Urey's contracts with the Navy. By July 1941 an OSRD contract was assigned to Dunning and his associates, and from then on funds were always available for the work. In May 1943 Urey was put in over-all charge and remained so until March 1945, when the laboratory was taken over from Columbia by Carbide and Carbon Chemicals Corporation.

The main point of the diffusion process is that to effect any real separation the gas must diffuse through many barriers. To get 99 per cent U-235 one needs about 4000 stages. One great virtue is that all the stages need not be traversed; therefore small experimental plants can be set up and tested.

The diffusing gas, uranium hexafluoride, has to be produced, pumps have to be designed and built, barriers have to be invented and tested. The latter involves a nice point. A proper diffusion barrier for the purpose cannot have holes larger than 4 ten-millionths of an inch in diameter. There must be billions of holes and they must not become enlarged or plugged during the diffusion. Naturally one should be able to make the barriers in large numbers and with uniform results. It is wonderful that such barriers were actually developed.

Finally early in 1943 most of the problems seemed sufficiently near solution so that large-scale plants could be built. In June 1943 the steam power plant that would furnish power for the diffusion plant was begun at Oak Ridge. It is one of the largest power plants of this sort ever built. The other buildings began going up three and four months later. Because of the unit nature of the process, the diffusion plant could be put into production as the sections were built. By the middle of 1944 it was going full strength.

The diffusion process had no dramatic moments such as the Chicago pile, or the Hanford plant. The men worked at the job between 1940 and 1945 with a courage and persistence that are admirable. They solved with wonderful ingenuity and scientific skill problems that seemed almost impossible. I gather that toward the end of 1945 the plant was producing on a sufficiently large scale to make it one of the significant contributors of fissile material.

In the early days of the uranium work, the two most promising separation methods were considered to be the gaseous diffusion process, and the centrifuge process. After 1941 the centrifuge method was studied intensively in two places. The magnitude of the engineering problems proved so great that no large-scale production was ever undertaken, and the method was discontinued.

Only the electromagnetic method of separation was left. The method is J. J. Thomson's old Geissler tubes writ large, and had been used by Aston in his mass spectroscope. It depends on the fact that in a powerful magnetic field a stream of ions will be deviated to a degree depending on the mass of the ions. Figure 20 on page 162 shows the principle. It will be recalled that with it Nier in 1939 had separated microscopic specks of U-235 from the other uranium isotopes for Dunning and his associates to see which isotope fissions. Nier's apparatus collected a maximum of 1 millionth of a gram of U-235 in a 24-hour day. The question was whether a larger magnet and better conditions could produce more. If so, how many units would be required to produce the necessary pounds of U-235?

The University of California had a piece of apparatus (a cyclotron—of no interest for us, except that it was an arrangement for making a beam of very fast protons) with a large magnet. Under the general direction of E. O. Lawrence the 37-inch magnet was set up for this purpose and by December 1941 it was functioning. In January 1942 it really made fair separations, and by March 1942 it was going so well that Lawrence's hopes seemed to be borne out.

A large research program was initiated in which many physicists were engaged, and this group was strengthened

by a British contingent under the leadership of M. L.
Oliphant from the University of Birmingham. A larger
magnet, with a pole diameter of 184 inches, was put to
work and around it were assembled shops and laboratories so that by May 1942 it was ready for use.

In several months of intensive experimentation it became clear that many such units would be required for
enough material to be produced to be of military importance. If one unit produces 1/100 gram a day, about
45,000 units would produce 1 pound per day. It was
merely a question of cost and time.

Remember that this was in September 1942. No chain
reaction had as yet been established and no plutonium
production had been initiated. The gaseous diffusion
method was promising but not spectacular. Obviously one
had to develop the magnetic separation process. Here too
the great virtue was that one unit could be built at a
time; it was not all or nothing.

The end of 1942 was the time of decision. The self-
sustaining chain reaction worked at Chicago. At that
time the plutonium plant at Oak Ridge was in the design
stage, and the gaseous diffusion plant at Oak Ridge was
decided on. At the same time an electromagnetic separation plant was approved for construction at Oak Ridge.
These three are now located on a tract near the Clinch
River, each plant in a separate valley.

Construction of the first group of units at Clinton began
in March 1943 and by the end of the year it was ready to

go. As improvements were made at California they were incorporated in the new units. During the winter of 1944-45 the electromagnetic separation plant was operating full scale and was producing U-235 in sufficient purity for the manufacture of atomic bombs.

4. THE ATOMIC BOMB IS BUILT

We are approaching the end of our story. From three different sources fissile material is being produced in high degree of purity. There is plutonium-239 from the Hanford plant; there is U-235 from the gaseous diffusion plant at Oak Ridge; and U-235 from the electromagnetic separation plant also at Oak Ridge. We must now use these materials to make an atomic bomb.

A self-sustaining, nuclear chain reaction in a pile such as worked in Chicago and at Hanford has a multiplication factor of 1.00. The fission of each atom of U-235 may release several neutrons, but only 1 of these reaches another U-235 atom to continue the chain. There may be 1 such chain or 1,000,000; that depends on the number of U-235 atoms initially set in fission by an outside source. The piles must be constantly watched from behind thick concrete walls to see that the multiplication factor remains at 1.00.

An atomic bomb is something different. Because it is composed of pure plutonium-239 or pure uranium-235, there is nothing to absorb neutrons except atoms that fission and produce more neutrons. All the neutrons that remain in the lump will result in fission. Assume that from each fissioning atom only 2 neutrons remain in the mass to be absorbed by other atoms. The multiplication factor will be 2.00, and each neutron generation will result in twice the number of splitting atoms than the preceding generation. The first atom that fissions produces 2 effective neutrons. These are absorbed by 2 atoms, which fission and produce 2 neutrons each, making a total of 4 neutrons. Each of these is absorbed by an atom that fissions, with a total result of 8 neutrons available. Thus the generations of splitting atoms number 1, 2, 4, 8, 16, 32, 64, 128, and so on.

Such a reproductive series increases at a fantastic rate. The 10th generation is 1024; the 20th generation is over a million; the 30th generation over a billion; the 60th generation is over a billion billion; the 90th generation is over a billion billion billion. Suppose each neutron generation lasts a millionth of a second. Then in 90 generations or 90 millionths of a second, over a billion billion billion atoms will have fissioned. In the minutest fraction of a second, the whole mass of material will have fissioned and released the energies that we know about. If an explosion is defined as the sudden release of a large amount of energy in a small space, then this is an explosion.

The important point is the critical mass. If a piece of uranium-235 or plutonium-239 is smaller than the critical mass, not enough neutrons will remain inside for the multiplication factor to reach 1.00, and when fission is initiated it will die out. If a piece is larger than the critical mass, then even if its multiplication factor is only slightly greater than 1.00 it will explode almost instantaneously after the first atom fissions because each atomic fission lasts less than a millionth of a second. Actually there are many stray neutrons around from cosmic rays, so that the mere accumulation of fissile material beyond the critical mass will instantly result in an explosion when one of these stray neutrons gets into the mass. Most of the technical troubles in producing the bomb actually came from the amazingly short time between the arrival of the first neutron and the explosion.

Essentially then, the construction of an atomic bomb is merely an arrangement for rapidly assembling a piece of pure Pu-239 or U-235 larger than the critical mass, and supplying it with a few neutrons. Imagine a mass of U-235 or of Pu-239 just smaller than the critical size. This will not explode even if we supply it with a few neutrons. Then imagine that we have a smaller piece of the same material at some distance. It too will not explode. But if it were added to the larger piece, the two would form a mass well above the critical size. Therefore just imagine a machine that can bring these two pieces together with great rapidity, and you have an atomic bomb. For instance, the smaller mass may be in the form of a bullet that can be shot from a distance of a few feet into a prepared hole in the larger mass, which is receiving a few neutrons. Almost at once after the bullet hits there will be an explosion.

What is the critical size? The earliest estimates back in 1939 had been between 2 and 200 pounds. These estimates were based on the available measurements of the distance that a neutron can go before it is captured, and on the distance that a neutron needs to be from a uranium nucleus in order to be captured by it—a factor called the "capture cross section" of the uranium nucleus. These were rough measurements and obviously needed careful going over. They would be needed the moment U-235 and Pu-239 became available, even for so simple a decision as how to store the material, in what sizes, and how far apart.

There were hundreds of such questions that needed investigation. How much energy will a bomb produce? Where should it be exploded, high in the air, under water, or on the ground? What will happen to the radioactive gases produced? Can one make a bomb smaller than the critical size provided neutron reflectors are placed around it? What are good neutron reflectors or tampers? Will the bomb fly apart before the chain reaction has finished, or can it be held together until all the atoms have fissioned? These questions could not wait until the last minute when Pu-239 or U-235 had become available. Nor, worse luck, could one try small bombs to see how they would work. With an atomic bomb it is all or nothing. The problem is thus one of combining the most accurate measurements with the best computation from theory.

Some of these matters were already under discussion in 1941. Early in 1942 Gregory Breit of the University of Wisconsin had initiated a number of experimental and theoretical studies at various institutions concerned with precisely such questions. Later that summer J. R. Oppenheimer of the University of California formed a group there for further theoretical studies and became the co-ordinator of all the experimental work. By the end of the summer of 1942 it seemed essential to set up a separate laboratory just for these purposes.

For secrecy and safety it was located on an isolated and deserted mesa thirty miles from Santa Fe, at Los Alamos, New Mexico. Oppenheimer became the director and arrived in March 1943. He assembled around him a great concentration of theoretical and experimental physicists and in an amazingly short time built what has since become probably the best equipped physics research laboratory in the world. He was joined by such familiar people as Hans Bethe, Enrico Fermi, Niels Bohr of Denmark, James Chadwick from Cambridge, England, who brought with him a whole British contingent, and dozens and dozens of other scientists all of whom worked in this Shangri-La.

There was a Theoretical Physics Division, an Experimental Nuclear Physics Division, a Chemistry and Metallurgy Division, an Ordnance Division, an Explosives

Division, a Bomb Physics Division, and an Advanced
Development Division, each under a well-known director.
Much of what they all did is still buried in secrecy. This
however is known. As the result of their labors they constructed atomic bombs that worked.

5. THE SECRET IS OUT

No theory is acceptable until it has been put to the
test of experiment. The theory that underlies the atomic
bomb is an elaborate structure that has grown from
simple beginnings. We started with salt dissolving in
water, which yielded the concept of atoms. Since then we
have enlarged and complicated this basic atom until its
architecture is a mass of whirling electrons in shell after
shell around a nucleus that has its own inner complexities
of neutrons, protons, and charges tied in knots by binding
energies.

Some time in the course of the story the reader has
probably said to himself that this theoretical piling of
Pelion on Olympus and of Ossa on Pelion is too much.
First we measure the combining ratios of substances.
They turn out to be almost whole numbers, and we have
an explanation. Then because they are not really whole
numbers we devise a theory to explain the differences:
we invent isotopes. But even in terms of the new theory
there still are differences from whole numbers, so we
invent packing factors. Then we invent fast neutrons and
slow neutrons and nuclear fission and capture cross sec-

tion. Finally we predict a theoretical atomic bomb, which cannot be demonstrated on a small scale. And we expect the world to supply hundreds of millions of dollars to build factories employing thousands of people to produce a few pounds of something that we insist must be kept in small packages.

It seems fantastic. It *is* fantastic. To the scientist who works daily in the laboratory in terms of a theory, it becomes a familiar reality. He watches it grow. He predicts a piece here or there, and either he or a colleague elsewhere tests it and finds it true or false. The whole structure gradually assumes a kind of certainty that to the outsider who has not followed its development, seems wholly visionary and a little mad.

The atomic bomb project was infinitely more complex than the usual scientific experiment. Ordinarily, the step from prediction to practice is not large or long delayed, and in the course of the development, progress can be established by small-scale experiments. With the atomic bomb the realization of theoretical prediction involved thousands of people, vast amounts of money, factories, towns, secrets, the Army, the Navy, and the highest echelons of Government and Science. And nothing to show for it until the final single all-or-nothing test.

Let no one imagine that the scientists and military men who assembled at Alamogordo in the earliest morning hours of July 16, 1945 were not fully conscious of these implications. More than this. The scientists knew that they were about to open a new age in human history. They had all wrestled with the problem during the war years. Many had even made official representations against the use of the bomb on civilian populations. Not only were the military and industrial implications evident to them, but they had envisaged the social and political repercussions to come. Here they were, making the experiment toward which all this thought and effort had been directed.

True to the canons of drama there was a final suspense. The whole mechanism had been machined with the utmost precision and was being assembled. For a few anguished moments, one part became wedged tightly and would not budge. Robert F. Bacher, originally of Cornell, who actually manipulated the assembly, remained coolest of all and succeeded in putting the parts together. From then on everything went according to schedule. The explosion took place, and emitted the light, heat, sound, radioactivity, and blast with which the world has since become familiar. The secret was out for all the world to see. An atomic bomb was possible.

This is the real point. We have all heard about the secrets of the atomic bomb, how they were guarded, and how important it is to keep or not to keep them to ourselves. There have even been spy scares about it. The reader knows now that there are no fundamental secrets. Atomic energy was known and evaluated in 1900; the basic equation was written in 1905. Its meaning in terms of atomic structure has come slowly with each new discovery about the nature of matter and energy. If there were a secret, we gave it away in July 1945. It is that a chain reaction is possible and that it can be used to make a bomb. That was the meaning of the explosion at Alamogordo.

Can another country make an atomic bomb? Of course it can. If we can think of several ways of doing each step from uranium fission to atomic bomb, so can another group of scientists. In fact, the British were ahead of us in 1941, and they may possibly have given us a good run if Britain were not so near Germany that its plants and cities were steadily bombed and blasted. We were far away from the scene of the war, and the British sent their best people to work with us. So did the Canadians. Even Niels Bohr from Denmark came here to help. Moreover, we had on our side some of the best brains in the refugees from Germany, Austria, Hungary, and Italy.

All these men and women worked against time and were always haunted by the possibility that the Germans might get there first, or that a chain reaction could not be established. Some of them hoped it could never be established. The social and political crises that lay ahead were all too clear and some of them hoped even against hope that some quirk of nature would make it impossible to have a chain reaction. Where that quirk was, no one knew. It might have turned up at any stage in the process and made further progress impossible. That uncertainty is gone. Alamogordo made it plain that a chain reaction with uranium and plutonium can work.

Of course there are technical and engineering secrets. They cannot involve anything fundamental. Most likely they are the kind that competing motorcar manufacturers keep from one another. In a short time competent engineers and inventors can duplicate them and probably improve them. This fact does not belittle the ingenuity, imagination, and skill involved in technical and engineering work. But it does insist that we Americans have no monopoly of such ingenuity, imagination, and skill.

The design of the actual bomb itself can be considered like the design of any other piece of ordnance. We keep the design of our submarines secret, also of our torpedoes, guns, bombsights, of practically every important piece of ordnance. Other countries do likewise. We can do so, or not; it is of no great matter. The real secret is that there is no basic secret.

EPILOGUE: THE FUTURE

Most of us who worked on the scientific side of the war were not happy under the secrecy and compartmentation imposed by the military. We accepted the security regulations voluntarily and kept them even when we saw that they interfered with the rapid progress of our work. We are glad to be free of the restrictions—those of us who are. We do not wish to see them perpetuated, because they stifle scientific achievement.

If further progress is to be made in understanding the structure of the atom and the nature of energy, if additional information is to be achieved along the road that we have traveled in this book, it can be done only in the same way as heretofore—by working on those problems freely and by sharing our knowledge with all others. Science cannot flourish in secrecy. The war is over, and to maintain our lead in scientific work, to keep up the production of that basic knowledge upon which all power and civilization depends, we must have the freedom to work and to publish.

Scientists know that in spite of all the ballyhoo about

the progress of science during the war, there was relatively little fundamental achievement. The story in this book shows that even in atomic energy what was accomplished during the war may be considered as a large and extensive footnote to the history of the scientific understanding of matter and energy. The basic facts were known before the war.

We can learn from this that much of the talk of pouring money into the cure and conquest of disease is irresponsible. Naturally we should spend money on the development and production of things like penicillin. But such money would have been wasted before Alexander Fleming discovered penicillin, and Howard Florey and Ernest Chain learned how to extract and purify it. As the body of knowledge increases and grows, so will its applications multiply. Where specific applications will arise for industry and for medicine, no one can tell in advance. But come they will if more knowledge becomes available.

With regard to atomic energy, practically all scientists are agreed that we must have international control. The Acheson-Lilienthal Report of the State Department gives us hope that with proper planning this can be achieved. No scientist wants to see bombs piled up with which to terrify the rest of the world. We all prefer fissionable materials to be used for peaceful purposes.

Too much, however, should not be made of the rosy future that atomic energy can give us. Power installations do not spend much on the coal that supplies the energy. Less than 10 per cent of the price of electricity depends upon the cost of coal. Thus even if coal were supplied for nothing, the costs of electricity and power would still not be very different from what they are at present. Atomic energy for industrial purposes is therefore a convenience. Piles for its production can be built in inaccessible places, remote from railroads and from transmission lines. It is best not to speculate about this. We have U-235 and Pu-239, which can produce energy. The properties of these materials should be investigated; what comes out will surely be interesting and may be revolutionary.

A wonderful tool has been made available, and vast stores of energy have been opened that can keep us going perhaps even after coal and oil reserves have been exhausted. It is significant to remember that ultimately the energy from coal, oil, and water power is atomic energy. Water power comes from the sun's heat; coal and oil are only the remains of ancient plants that grew by the light of the sun. The light and heat of the sun are ours from the atomic transformation of hydrogen into helium. Now we need no longer use green plants alone to capture the atomic energy released in the sun; we can release it ourselves by the fission of uranium.

All this, however, is idle speculation and fancy dreaming so long as the threat of war hangs over us. Man really has his fate in his hands. If he can put into the practice of world relations the same honesty, the same courage, the same intellect, and the same drive that have gone into science and the accumulation of knowledge, then the future will indeed be a happy one. If he cannot, then anyone can envision the hell that may be on earth. The menace of total destruction, the horror of partial survival, the distortion of daily life that the new weapons envisage may easily convert an uncertain political and economic environment into what Castiglioni calls a "collective anguish" comparable to the tenth century's terror of the world's end.

Only the conviction of a just and stable peace, the removal of fear and tension, and the recognition of all men's right to survive regardless of color and creed can make a world in which atomic energy can be properly used.

Whether these desiderata can be achieved by the continued division of the world into sovereign and independent nations is dubious. We live on the continuous but finite surface of a sphere of which any part can be reached from any other part in a few hours. It is obsolete to suppose that such a surface can be artificially maintained in a fractional state of national groups, each determined to keep its peculiar economy free from influence by the others. The sooner all peoples join in some law-abiding extranational order, the better for us who hope for civilization. If the advent of atomic energy succeeds in making us acutely aware of the need for a legal world order, it will have been good, in spite of its horrid face at Hiroshima. I hope the future will see it as good.

INDEX

INDEX

Adams, Henry, 52
Air (free and fixed), 17-19
Alamogordo (N. M.), 188, 190
Alkali metals, 24, 31, 72, 73
Alpha particles, 55, 56, 61, 129
    as helium, 56, 61
    collisions of, 61
    streams of, 59, 60, 65, 66,
      102
Alpha rays, 55
Aluminum, 123
    for canning, 176
    ion, 45
Amber, 39
Anderson, Carl D., 107, 137,
    169
Argon, 29, 91
Aston, Francis W., 92, 93, 95,
    97, 98, 99, 114, 139, 140,
    164, 180
Atom, 9, 11
    critical mass, 148, 183-84
Atomic
    bomb, 118, 119
      composition, 182, 184
      construction, 184
      critical size, 147, 148
      explosion, 3, 4, 189
      idea, 6

bonds, 35, 36, 38, 57
energy, 57
    control, 193
    implications, 189
    legislation, 4
    release, 136
    secrets, 5
factory, 171
number, 32, 33, 66, 67
nucleus, 58, 66, 67
research, appropriations for,
    153, 154
particles, velocity of, 129,
    130
power, 194
structure, 33, 44, 46, 60, 66
    further research, 192
theory, 20
transformation, 117
volume, 32
weights, 17, 20, 23, 66, 67
    as whole numbers, 22,
      23, 80, 95
Automatic machinery, 177

Bacher, Robert F., 189
Bainbridge, K. T., 8, 95, 97
Barium, 133, 136, 138
Barriers, gaseous diffusion, 179

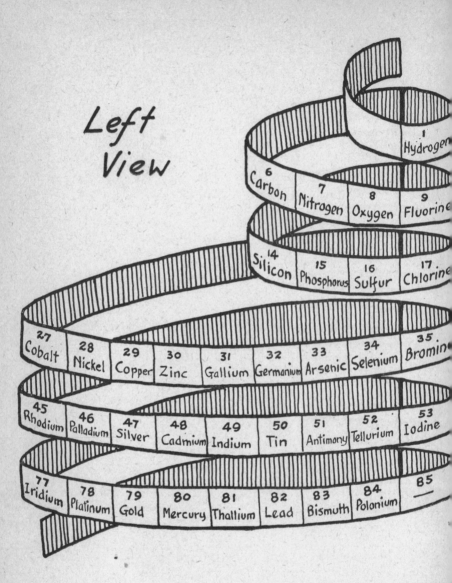

Left
View

1
Hydrogen

6
Carbon

7
Nitrogen

8
Oxygen

9
Fluorine

14
Silicon

15
Phosphorus

16
Sulfur

17
Chlorine

27
Cobalt

28
Nickel

29
Copper

30
Zinc

31
Gallium

32
Germanium

33
Arsenic

34
Selenium

35
Bromine

45
Rhodium

46
Palladium

47
Silver

48
Cadmium

49
Indium

50
Tin

51
Antimony

52
Tellurium

53
Iodine

77
Iridium

78
Platinum

79
Gold

80
Mercury

81
Thallium

82
Lead

83
Bismuth

84
Polonium

85
—

THE PERIODIC TABLE